TEACHER EDITION

GO MATH!

Printed in U.S.A.

ISBN 978-0-547-59235-0

10 11 12 13 14 0877 20 19 18 17 16 15 14 13

4500403701   B C D E F G

 HOUGHTON MIFFLIN HARCOURT

 **Number and Operations**

COMMON CORE CRITICAL AREA Representing, relating, and operating on whole numbers, initially with sets of objects.

Domain: Counting and Cardinality   CC.K.CC

Lessons   **Grade K Common Core State Standards**

8.1   **Count to tell the number of objects.**
CC.K.CC.5   Count to answer "how many?" questions about as many as 20 things arranged in a line, a rectangular array, or a circle, or as many as 10 things in a scattered configuration; given a number from 1 to 20 count out that many objects.

8.2   **Know number names and the count sequence.**
CC.K.CC.3   Write numbers from 0 to 20. Represent a number of objects with a written numeral 0 to 20 (with 0 representing a count of no objects).

8.3   **Know number names and the count sequence.**
CC.K.CC.2   Count forward beginning from a given number within the known sequence (instead of having to begin at 1).

8.4   **Compare numbers.**
CC.K.CC.6   Identify whether the number of objects in one group is greater than, less than, or equal to the number of objects in another group, e.g., by using matching and counting strategies.

8.5–8.8   **Know number names and the count sequence.**
CC.K.CC.1   Count to 100 by ones and tens.

Table of Contents

Chapter 8   Represent, Count, and Write 20 and Beyond

 Domain:
Counting and Cardinality   CC.K.CC

 Mathematical Practices:
CC.K–12.MP.4   Model with mathematics.
CC.K–12.MP.5   Use appropriate tools strategically.

* This chapter also includes the following standards: K.CC.4a, K.CC.4b, K.CC.4c

Chapter At A Glance

Domain: Counting and Cardinality

Chapter Essential Question How can you show, count, and write numbers to 20 and beyond?

Use the Chapter Planner in the *Go Math! Planning Guide* for pacing.

Lesson At A Glance

	LESSON 8.1 CC.K.CC.5	**LESSON 8.2** CC.K.CC.3	**LESSON 8.3** CC.K.CC.2
	Hands On • Model and Count 20 ...... 309A	**Count and Write 20** 313A	**Count and Order to 20** 317A
Essential Question	How can you show and count 20 objects?	How can you count and write 20 with words and numbers?	How can you count forward to 20 from a given number?
Objective	Model and count 20 with objects.	Represent 20 objects with a number name and a written numeral.	Count forward to 20 from a given number.
Vocabulary	twenty	twenty	one, two, three, four, five, six, seven, eight, nine, ten, eleven, twelve, thirteen, fourteen, fifteen, sixteen, seventeen, eighteen, nineteen, twenty
Materials	MathBoard, connecting cubes, Counting Tape	MathBoard, Counting Tape	MathBoard, connecting cubes, Counting Tape

Print Resources

8.1 Student Edition	**8.2 Student Edition**	**8.3 Student Edition**
8.1 Standards Practice Book	**8.2 Standards Practice Book**	**8.3 Standards Practice Book**
8.1 Reteach	8.2 Reteach	8.3 Reteach
8.1 Enrich	8.2 Enrich	8.3 Enrich
Grab-and-Go™ Centers Kit	**Grab-and-Go™ Centers Kit**	**Grab-and-Go™ Centers Kit**
ELL Strategy • Draw	**ELL** Strategy • Define	**ELL** Strategy • Model Language

Digital Path

8.1 *e*Student Edition	**8.2 *e*Student Edition**	**8.3 *e*Student Edition**
8.1 *e*Teacher Edition	**8.2 *e*Teacher Edition**	**8.3 *e*Teacher Edition**
Animated Math Models	Animated Math Models	Animated Math Models
iT iTools	*iT* iTools	*iT* iTools
MM HMH Mega Math	MM HMH Mega Math	MM HMH Mega Math

RtI — Response to Intervention

Before the Chapter	**During the Lesson**	**After the Chapter**
✓ Show What You Know	✓ Share and Show	✓ Chapter Review/Test
• Prerequisite Skills Activities	• RtI Activities	• RtI Activities
• Soar to Success Math	• Mid-Chapter Checkpoint	• Soar to Success Math
	• Soar to Success Math	

EVERY DAY COUNTS®

Use every day to develop computational fluency.
Visit www.greatsource.com/everydaycounts

Assess Depth of Knowledge

See Chapter 8 Performance Task and Assessment *Guide*.

LESSON 8.4 CC.K.CC.6

Problem Solving • Compare Numbers to 20 .... 321A

How can you solve problems using the strategy *make a model*?

Solve problems by using the strategy *make a model.*

compare, one, two, three, four, five, six, seven, eight, nine, ten, eleven, twelve, thirteen, fourteen, fifteen, sixteen, seventeen, eighteen, nineteen, twenty

MathBoard, connecting cubes, Counting Tape

LESSON 8.5 CC.K.CC.1

Count to 50 by Ones 325A

How does the order of numbers help you to count to 50 by ones?

Know the count sequence when counting to 50 by ones.

fifty

MathBoard, Counting Tape

LESSON 8.6 CC.K.CC.1

Count to 100 by Ones 329A

How does the order of numbers help you to count to 100 by ones?

Know the count sequence when counting to 100 by ones.

one hundred

MathBoard, Counting Tape

8.4 Student Edition

8.4 Standards Practice Book

8.4 Reteach

8.4 Enrich

Grab-and-Go™ Centers Kit

ELL **Strategy** • Restate

8.5 Student Edition

8.5 Standards Practice Book

8.5 Reteach

8.5 Enrich

Grab-and-Go™ Centers Kit

ELL **Strategy** • Identify Patterns

8.6 Student Edition

8.6 Standards Practice Book

8.6 Reteach

8.6 Enrich

Grab-and-Go™ Centers Kit

ELL **Strategy** • Model Concepts

8.4 *eStudent Edition*

8.4 *eTeacher Edition*

📺 **Animated Math Models**

iT *iTools*

𝕄𝕄 **HMH Mega Math**

8.5 *eStudent Edition*

8.5 *eTeacher Edition*

8.6 *eStudent Edition*

8.6 *eTeacher Edition*

📺 **Animated Math Models**

iT *iTools*

GREAT ON INTERACTIVE WHITEBOARD!

Digital Path 🖱

📺 Animated Math Models   𝕄𝕄 HMH Mega Math   A·BC Multimedia *e*Glossary   Soar to Success Math

✓ Assessment   *iT* *iTools*   📱 Professional Development Video Podcasts

Chapter At A Glance

Domain: Counting and Cardinality

Lesson At A Glance

LESSON 8.7 CC.K.CC.1

Count to 100 by Tens 333A

Essential Question	How can you count to 100 by tens on a hundred chart?
Objective	Know the count sequence when counting to 100 by tens.
Vocabulary	**tens**
Materials	MathBoard, Counting Tape

LESSON 8.8 CC.K.CC.1

Count by Tens ... 337A

Essential Question	How can you use sets of tens to count to 100?
Objective	Use sets of tens to count to 100.
Vocabulary	tens
Materials	MathBoard, Counting Tape

Teacher Notes

Print Resources

Lesson 8.7
- 8.7 Student Edition
- 8.7 Standards Practice Book
- 8.7 Reteach
- 8.7 Enrich
- Grab-and-Go™ Centers Kit
- **ELL** Strategy • Describe

Lesson 8.8
- 8.8 Student Edition
- 8.8 Standards Practice Book
- 8.8 Reteach
- 8.8 Enrich
- Grab-and-Go™ Centers Kit
- **ELL** Strategy • Model Concepts

Digital Path

Lesson 8.7
- 8.7 eStudent Edition
- 8.7 eTeacher Edition
- Animated Math Models
- iTools

Lesson 8.8
- 8.8 eStudent Edition
- 8.8 eTeacher Edition
- Chapter 8 Test
- Animated Math Models
- iTools

Assessment

Diagnostic	Formative	Summative
• Show What You Know • Diagnostic Interview Task • Soar to Success Math	• Lesson Quick Check • Mid-Chapter Checkpoint	• Chapter Review/Test • Performance Assessment • Chapter Test • Online Assessment

Teacher Notes

Teaching for Depth

by Juli K. Dixon
Professor of Mathematics Education
University of Central Florida
Orlando, Florida

Representations and Counting

It is important for children to build on their knowledge of numbers from 0 to 20 and extend their number understanding to 100.

- Ten frames and connecting cubes are used to model 20. Children record the the number 20 as the numeral 20 and the word *twenty* to build understanding.

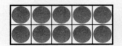 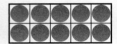 

- Writing the missing numbers in the sequence of 1 to 20 helps reinforce children's learning.

Count and Order Numbers to 100

A hundred chart extends children's ability to count to 100 and to identify number patterns shown on the hundred chart.

- Children should use a hundred chart to count. After counting, they compare the positions of numbers on the hundred chart by using the phrases *greater than* and *less than*.

- Children compare sets by counting and then recording the number of objects in each set. Then they can identify the set that has more or fewer objects.

Representation

Multiple representations for numbers promote learning. Therefore, children need a variety of experiences with representing numbers. These may include physical objects, word names, drawings, and numerals.

From the Research

" …[C]hildren need multiple experiences with not only visual representations of number and quantity, but also physical and aural representations. Pairing these representations with verbal expression—often in a descriptive dialogue of questions and statements—helps interpret and encode information so that it can be anchored with a child's knowledge framework for later retrieval. "
(Martinez & Martinez, 2007, p. 104)

Mathematical Practices

Children use ten frames and the hundred chart to extend their experiences representing, counting, and writing numbers to 20 and beyond. Ten frames and counters are useful for showing 20, while the hundred chart is useful for counting to 100 by ones and tens. Using ten frames and the hundred chart helps children see how different tools can support their thinking. These experiences will help children **use appropriate tools strategically**.

PODCASTING

Professional Development Video Podcasts:
The Meaning of Addition and Subtraction, Grades K–2, Segment 1

Cross-Curricular Center Activities

How Many Wheels?

Objective Children count the number of wheels on more than one vehicle.

Materials toy vehicles, chart with two rows labeled *Number of _____*, *Number of Wheels*

- **Look at the car. How many wheels are on one car? If the car had three wheels, would it be able to go?**
- Show four more cars. Have children write the number of cars in the top row of the chart. Have children draw a dot on the bottom row of the chart for each wheel they see on the cars. Then have them count the dots.
- Have partners repeat the activity for different numbers of cars or other vehicles, such as tricycles or bicycles.

Number of cars	
Number of Wheels	

Social Studies Center

Let's Make Flags

Objective Children count stars and stripes and make an American flag.

Materials seven red paper stripes and six white paper stripes (pre-cut), blue paper rectangle tape or glue

- Display an American flag or a picture of the flag.
- **How many red stripes? How many white stripes? How many stripes in all?** Explain that the 13 stripes stand for the 13 colonies that began our country.
- Count the number of stars together. **There is one star for each state. Which state do we live in?**
- Have partners assemble the flag and draw 50 stars to complete it.

Art Center

Birds on a Wire

Objective Children draw and count birds.

Materials drawing paper

- Draw a horizontal line across the length of a sheet of paper. Draw 17 birds on the line. **Do you think I drew 20 birds, fewer than 20 birds, or more than 20 birds? How can we check?**
- Count the birds with children to find out how many.
- Have each partner draw birds on a wire and then show his or her picture. Ask the other partner to guess how many and count to find the number.

Review Prerequisite Skills

 **Activities**

Model Teen Numbers   TIER 2

Objective Represent teen numbers with counters and numerals.

Materials two-color counters, two Ten Frames, Number and Symbol Tiles (front) (see *eTeacher Resources*)

Give children two ten frames. Ask them to fill the first ten frame with counters.

- **If you want to show 11, how many counters do you place in the second ten frame?** 1

Have children place one counter in the second ten frame.

- **Look at the ten frames. How many ones in the first ten frame?** 10 **How many ones in the second ten frame?** 1 **So 10 ones and 1 one make 11.**

Then guide children to show the number 11 with number tiles. Have them overlap the 10 tile with the 1 tile to form the numeral 11. Continue this process with children for numbers 12 to 19.

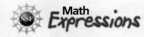 **Math Expressions**

Model from *Math Expressions*. For more information visit www.eduplace.com/hmhschool/mathexpressions

Number Riddles   TIER 2

Objective Identify teen numbers.

Materials Numeral Cards (8–15), (16–23), Counters and Numerals (9–12), (13–16), (17–20), (see *eTeacher Resources*)

Display the numeral cards for 11 to 19 and present riddles for the numbers. Have children take turns identifying the numbers and holding the counters and numerals cards for the answers.

Use riddles such as the following:

- **This number is 10 and 2 more. What is it?** 12
  This number is 10 and 7 more. What is it? 17

When all the cards have been identified, have children with cards line up in order from 11 to 19.

11	12	13	14	15
16	17	18	19	

COMMON CORE   Common Core State Standards Across the Grades

Before	Grade K	After
• Use counting and numbers to determine quantities up to 10. • Use counting and numbers to compare quantities. • Use one-to-one correspondence to compare quantities.	**Domain: Counting and Cardinality** Know number names and the count sequence. **CC.K.CC.1, CC.K.CC.2, CC.K.CC.3** Count to tell the number of objects. **CC.K.CC.5** Compare numbers. **CC.K.CC.6**	**Domain: Number and Operations in Base Ten** Extend the counting sequence. **CC.1.NBT.1** Understand place value. **CC.1.NBT.2, CC.1.NBT.3** Use place value understanding and properties of operations to add and subtract. **CC.1.NBT.4, CC.1.NBT.5, CC.1.NBT.6**

See A page of each lesson for Common Core Standard text.

Developing Math Language

Chapter Vocabulary

tens sets of 10 ones

twenty 1 ten and 10 ones

fifty 5 sets of 10 ones

one hundred 10 sets of 10 ones

one, two, three, four, five, six, seven, eight, nine, ten, eleven, twelve, thirteen, fourteen, fifteen, sixteen, seventeen, eighteen, nineteen, compare

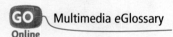 Multimedia eGlossary

ELL Vocabulary Activity

Objective Understand the vocabulary word *twenty*.

Materials Vocabulary card for *twenty* (see *eTeacher Resources*), counters or other small objects

Have children take turns modeling the number 20 with counters or other small objects. They should place a vocabulary card next to each model. Point out that the counters can be arranged in different ways to make twenty.

Practice vocabulary by using question strategies, such as:

Beginning
- **What number does this card represent?** 20

Intermediate
- Have children place 20 objects on the table. Have them count forward from 10.

Advanced
- **What number is one less than 20?** 19
- **What number is two less than 20?** 18

Vocabulary Strategy • Graphic Organizer

Materials Word Analysis graphic organizer (see *eTeacher Resources*)

Have children complete the Word Analysis graphic organizer using the vocabulary word *twenty*. In one column, they should define the word. In the next column, they should draw a picture.

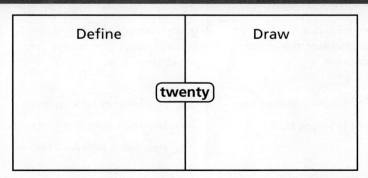

Define	Draw
(twenty)	

Chapter 8

Introduce the Chapter

Watermelon is actually a vegetable and not a fruit.

- **How many seeds can you count on this watermelon?** 24

Additional facts about watermelons:

- **Watermelons are related to cucumbers, pumpkins, and squash.**
- **Some watermelons are seedless.**

Ask the following question to guide children to an answer.

- **If you placed one counter for each seed in the picture in the ten frames, how many ten frames would you fill completely?** 2 **How many counters would you place in the third ten frame?** 4

Chapter 8 Represent, Count, and Write 20 and Beyond

Curious About Math with *Curious George*

Watermelon is actually a vegetable and not a fruit.

- How many seeds can you count on this watermelon? 24

Intervention Options  RtI Response to Intervention

Use Show What You Know, Lesson Quick Check, and Assessments to diagnose children's intervention levels.

TIER 1

On-Level Intervention

For children who are generally at grade level but need early intervention with the lesson concepts, use:

- ▲ Tier 1 Activity for every lesson
- ⭐ Soar to Success Math

TIER 2

Strategic Intervention

For children who need small group instruction to review concepts and skills needed for the chapter, use:

- ▲ Tier 2 Activity for every lesson
- GO Online Strategic Intervention Guide
- ▲ Prerequisite Skills Activities
- ⭐ Soar to Success Math

TIER 3

Intensive Intervention

For children who need one-on-one instruction to build foundational skills for the chapter, use:

- GO Online Intensive Intervention Guide
- ⭐ Soar to Success Math

ENRICHMENT

Independent Activities

For children who successfully complete lessons, use:

Grab-and-Go!

Differentiated Centers Kit

- Enrich Activity for every lesson
- Enrich Book
- MM HMH Mega Math

Name _____

Show What You Know ✓

Explore Numbers to 10

① (dots in ovals)

② (dots in ovals)

Compare Numbers to 10

③ (apples) 10 (tomatoes) ⑧

Write Numbers to 10

④ 3 4 5 6 7 8

DIRECTIONS 1. Circle all of the sets that show 9. 2. Circle all of the sets that show 8. 3. Count and tell how many. Write the number. Circle the number that is less. 4. Write the numbers in order as you count forward.

FAMILY NOTE: This page checks your child's understanding of important skills needed for success in Chapter 8.

306 three hundred six

© Houghton Mifflin Harcourt Publishing Company

GO Online Assessment Options
Soar to Success Math

Assessing Prior Knowledge

Have children complete on their own **Show What You Know.** Tested items are the prerequisite skills of this chapter.

Diagnostic Interview Task

The alternative interview tasks below evaluate children's understanding of each **Show What You Know** skill. The diagnostic chart may be used for intervention on prerequisite skills.

Materials two-color counters, Counters and Numerals (9–12), Ten Frames (see *eTeacher Resources*)

For evaluation checklist, see *Assessment Guide.*

Have the child count out eight counters and arrange them in two rows.

• **How many counters are there?** 8

Have the child arrange the same eight counters into three rows and count. Point out that the arrangement changed, but the number did not.

Place ten counters on a ten frame. Place eight counters on a second ten frame.

• **Which ten frame has fewer counters?**
The one with eight counters.

Display the counters and numerals cards non-sequentially. Ask the child to order the numbers from least to greatest.

✓ Show What You Know • Diagnostic Assessment

Use to determine if children need intervention for the chapter's prerequisite skills.

Were children successful with Show What You Know?

If NO...then
INTERVENE

If YES...then use
INDEPENDENT
ACTIVITIES

	Skill	Missed More Than	Intervene With	Soar to Success Math
TIER 3	Explore Numbers to 10	1	*Intensive Intervention User Guide,* Activity 8	Warm-Up 2.09
TIER 2	Compare Numbers to 10	1	*Strategic Intervention Skill 7*	Warm-Up 7.06
TIER 2	Write Numbers to 10	2	*Strategic Intervention Skill 8*	Warm-Up 2.09

Grab-and-Go!™

Differentiated Centers Kit

Use the *Enrich Book* or the independent activities in the *Grab-and-Go™ Differentiated Centers Kit.*

Vocabulary Builder

Children use multiple strategies to develop grade-appropriate vocabulary.

Have children complete the activities on this page by working alone or with partners.

Have children point to each sea otter as they count them aloud.

- **How many sea otters are there?** 18
- **Draw a line under the number word that shows how many sea otters in all.**
- **How many sea otters are wearing glasses?** 15
- **Write the number.** 15 **Circle the number word that shows how many sea otters are wearing sunglasses.**
- **Are there more sea otters wearing sunglasses or more sea otters without sunglasses?** more sea otters with sunglasses

Name _____

Vocabulary Builder

eighteen

15
fifteen

DIRECTIONS Point to each otter as you count. Point to the number word that shows how many otters in all. How many are wearing glasses? Write the number.

© Houghton Mifflin Harcourt Publishing Company

GO Online • eStudent Edition • Multimedia eGlossary

Chapter 8

three hundred seven **307**

Literature Big Book

One Moose, Twenty Mice
by Clare Beaton
reinforces counting up to 20
objects for Chapter 8.

Game
Who Has More?

Player 1

Player 2

© Houghton Mifflin Harcourt Publishing Company

DIRECTIONS Play with a partner. Each player shuffles a set of numeral cards and places them facedown in a stack. Each player turns over the top card on his or her stack and models that number by placing cube trains on the work space. Partners compare the cube trains. The player with the greater number keeps both of the numeral cards. If both numbers are the same, each player returns the card to the bottom of his or her stack. The player with the most cards at the end of the game wins.

MATERIALS 2 sets of numeral cards 11–20, cubes

308 three hundred eight

Game Who Has More?

▶ Using the Game

Set up a game center in the classroom. Include *Who Has More?* where children will model numbers 11–20 along with the materials needed to play.

Materials Numeral Cards (8–15), (16–23) (see *eTeacher Resources*), connecting cubes

Use numeral cards 11–20. Have children play in pairs. Each player shuffles a set of numeral cards and places them facedown in a stack. Each player turns over the top card on his or her stack and models that number by placing cube trains on the work space.

Partners compare the cube trains. The player with the greater number keeps both of the numeral cards. If both numbers are the same, each player returns the card to the bottom of his or her stack. The player with the most cards at the end of the game wins.

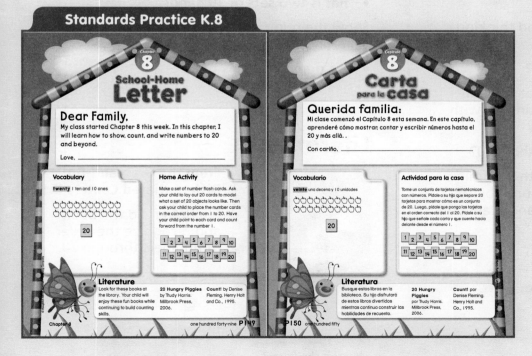

School-Home Letter available in English and Spanish in the *Standards Practice Book*, pp. P149–P150

The letter provides families with an overview of the math in the chapter, math vocabulary, an activity, and literature to read together.

Hands On • Model and Count 20

LESSON AT A GLANCE

Common Core Standard

Count to tell the number of objects.
CC.K.CC.5 Count to answer "how many?" questions about as many as 20 things arranged in a line, a rectangular array, or a circle, or as many as 10 things in a scattered configuration; given a number from 1–20, count out that many objects.

Also CC.K.CC.3, CC.K.CC.4a, CC.K.CC.4b

Lesson Objective
Model and count 20 with objects.

Essential Question
How can you show and count 20 objects?

Vocabulary twenty

Materials MathBoard, connecting cubes

Digital Path

☑ Animated Math Models

𝖬𝖬 HMH Mega Math

iT *i*Tools: Counters

GO MATH eStudent Edition

 COMMON CORE **PROFESSIONAL DEVELOPMENT**

About the Math

Teaching for Depth

As children work, encourage conversation and thinking with questions such as the following:

• **How can you tell that there are 20 objects?**

Children may answer this by pointing out that two full ten frames are 20 or two sets of 10, by counting, or with other responses.

• **How do you know how many to draw to show 20?**

Children may know that they need to fill both ten frames to make 20 or two sets of 10, or they may count objects that are shown and then continue to count and draw until they have reached 20.

PODCASTING **Professional Development Video Podcasts**

Daily Routines

Math Board

Common Core

SPIRAL REVIEW

Problem of the Day

 eTransparency 8.1

CALENDAR **Calendar Math** Count the dates to 19 on a class calendar. Point to the date after 19. What is the date? **What is the name of the day of the week for this date?**

20; name depends on current calendar

Fluency Builder

Materials Numeral Cards (16–23) (see *eTeacher Resources*)

Twenty

Lead children in rote counting to 19.

• **The next number when you count is 20. The number 20 follows 19 when you count.**

Lead children in counting to 20.

Have five children raise both hands and lead the class in counting them—10 hands. Have another five children raise both hands and count forward from 10 to 20 hands.

• **That is two sets of 10 hands.**

Show the numeral card for 20 and have children read it.

• **This number means two sets of 10.**

Literature

From the Grab-and-Go™ Differentiated Centers Kit

Children read the book and recognize the order of numbers through 20.

Where's the Party?

Differentiated Instruction Activities

ELL Language Support
Kinesthetic
Small Group

Strategy: Draw

Children can demonstrate their understanding by drawing rather than by using language.

- Have children draw a picture of the outdoors. Then ask them to draw grass in the picture.

- Tell children to draw 20 flowers in one line on the grass.

- Ask children to draw a dot on each flower as they count them aloud.

- Repeat this activity with a tree and 20 leaves in one line on a branch, if time permits.

See **ELL** Activity Guide for leveled activities.

Enrich
Auditory
Small Group

Have children show the number 20 by drawing and counting. Distribute three sheets of paper to each child.

- Let children choose an object to draw. Have children draw a different way to show 20 objects on each sheet of paper. Possible answers: two sets of 10 stars; 10 sets of two oranges; one set of 20 oranges; four sets of five oranges.

- Have partners share their drawings and show how they counted to 20.

RtI Response to Intervention

Reteach Tier 1
Kinesthetic / Verbal
Whole Class / Small Group

Help children review 20 by counting themselves.

- Stand in a circle with children. Model and explain the activity.

- Turn to the child next to you and shake the child's hand. **I am number 1. You must be number 2.**

- Continue with all the children in the circle until you reach 20.

- Repeat the activity, starting with a different child as number 1.

Tier 2
Kinesthetic / Visual / Verbal
Small Group

Materials chart paper, self-stick dots

Prepare two ten frames on chart paper.

- **You can practice counting and modeling numbers to 20 together.**

- Have children take turns adding a dot to the ten frame, one square at a time. Have children count the number of dots on their turn.

- Continue in the same way until the chart shows 20 dots.

- **How can you describe 20?** two full ten frames; two sets of 10; the number after 19

1 ENGAGE

Access Prior Knowledge Have children count from 1 to 18.

• **What number comes after 18?** 19

Ask children to draw 10 counters on the top ten frame of their Mathboard.

• **What do you know about a full ten frame?** It has 10.

• **Now draw nine counters in the other ten frame. How many counters is 10 and 9 more?** 19

2 TEACH and TALK

▶ **Listen and Draw**

Materials connecting cubes

Read aloud this problem as children listen.

Marla has 20 grapes. If Marla pretends that connecting cubes are grapes, how can she model 20 by using ten frames?

Count out 20 cubes with the children and ask them to fill the top frame.

• **How many cubes fill the top ten frame?** 10

• **How many cubes are left?** 10 **Place the cubes that are left in the bottom ten frame.**

• **How many cubes fill the bottom ten frame?** 10

• **How many cubes fill 2 ten frames?** 20

• **Count the cubes together.**

Reread the problem.

• **How can Marla model 20 by using cubes and ten frames?** She can model 10 in the top ten frame and 10 in the bottom ten frame.

• **Are there any cubes left?** no **How many full ten frames do you need to model 20 cubes?** two

Have children draw the cubes in the ten frames.

COMMON CORE

CC.K.CC.5 Count to answer "how many?" questions about as many as 20 things arranged in a line, a rectangular array, or a circle, or as many as 10 things in a scattered configuration; given a number from 1–20, count out that many objects.

Name _____

Model and Count 20

Essential Question How can you show and count 20 objects?

HANDS ON
Lesson 8.1

COMMON CORE STANDARD CC.K.CC.5
Count to tell the number of objects.

Listen and Draw

DIRECTIONS Use cubes to model 20. Draw the cubes.

Chapter 8 • Lesson 1   three hundred nine **309**

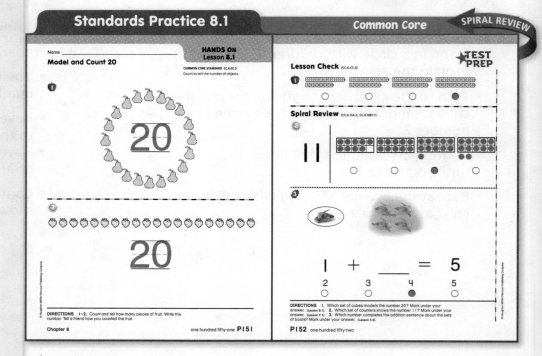

Standards Practice 8.1   **Common Core**   SPIRAL REVIEW

Share and Show

20
twenty

Check children's work.

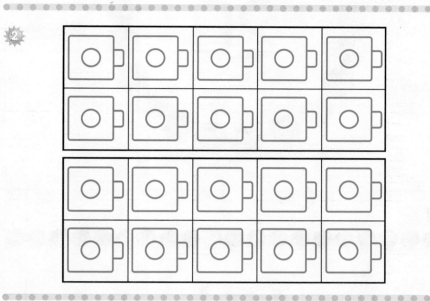

DIRECTIONS 1. Count and tell how many. Trace the number.
2. Use cubes to model the number 20. Draw the cubes. **3.** Use the
cubes from Exercise 2 to model ten-cube trains. Draw the cube trains.

310 three hundred ten

© Houghton Mifflin Harcourt Publishing Company

Reteach 8.1 ▲ RtI

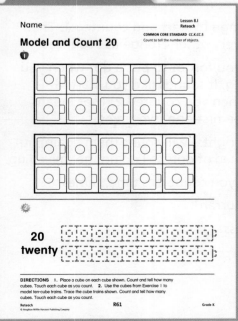

Name _____

Model and Count 20

COMMON CORE STANDARD CC.K.CC.5
Count to tell the number of objects.

20
twenty

DIRECTIONS 1. Place a cube on each cube shown. Count and tell how many
cubes. Touch each cube as you count. 2. Use the cubes from Exercise 1 to
model ten-cube trains. Trace the cube trains shown. Count and tell how many
cubes. Touch each cube as you count.

Reteach R61 Grade K
© Houghton Mifflin Harcourt Publishing Company

Enrich 8.1

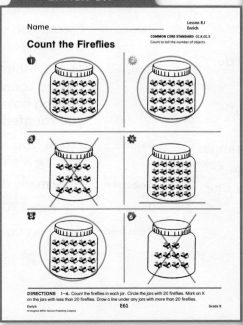

Name _____

Count the Fireflies

COMMON CORE STANDARD CC.K.CC.5
Count to tell the number of objects.

DIRECTIONS 1–6. Count the fireflies in each jar. Circle the jars with 20 fireflies. Mark an X
on the jars with less than 20 fireflies. Draw a line under any jars with more than 20 fireflies.

Enrich E61 Grade K

---

③ PRACTICE 🔲 Math Board

▶ **Share and Show** • **Guided Practice**

- **Look at Exercise 1. What number and number word do you see?** 20, *twenty*
- **How many orange halves are in the first set?** 10 **How many orange halves are in the second set?** 10 **How can you describe the two sets?** Possible answers: There are 20 in all. There are two sets of 10 oranges.

Give directions for tracing the number 20.

- **Look at Exercise 2. How can you model the number 20 with your cubes?** I can put 10 cubes in the top ten frame and 10 cubes in the bottom ten frame. **Place and draw the cubes.**

For Exercise 3, ask children to build two ten-cube trains. Count the cubes together.

- **How many cubes do you have if you have two ten-cube trains?** 20
- **Explain how you know you have 20.** I have 20 because there are 2 tens and I know that 2 tens are 20.
- **How many tens are in 20?** 2

Have children locate Exercise 3 and draw two ten-cube trains in the space.

Use Exercise 3 for **Quick Check.**

✓ Quick Check RtI

If ➤ a child misses Exercise 3

Then ➤ **Differentiate Instruction** with
- RtI Tier 1 Activity, p. 309B
- Reteach 8.1
- ✦ Soar to Success Math 1.09

⚠ COMMON ERRORS

Error Children may not recognize that two filled ten frames are 20.

Example Children say the number 10 for the 2 ten frames of cubes.

Springboard to Learning Together with children, count aloud the cubes in the first ten frame. Explain that the counting will continue even though they are moving to another ten frame. Continue counting from 11 to 20 on the second ten frame.

▶ More Practice

Point out the oranges in Exercise 4. Guide children in counting objects placed in a circle.

- **Choose one orange to start with. Draw a dot on each orange as you count. That way, you will see when to stop counting.**
- **How many oranges?** 20 **Write the number.**
- **Tell a friend how you counted the oranges.**

Use a similar process for Exercise 5. Encourage children to start counting from the beginning of the row.

- **How many plums are there?** 20 **Write the number.**
- **Tell a friend how you counted the plums.**

H.O.T. Problem Andy has two bunches of 10 grapes. Chad has 10 bunches of two grapes. Who has more grapes? They both have the same number of grapes.

Go Deeper

Children are now using what they know about the number 20 to solve a word problem.

Have children draw a picture on their MathBoards to solve the H.O.T. Problem. Encourage them to find other ways to show **20 grapes.** Possible answers: four bunches of five grapes; five bunches of four grapes

---

Name _____

© Houghton Mifflin Harcourt Publishing Company

DIRECTIONS 4–5. Count and tell how many pieces of fruit. Write the number. Tell a friend how you counted the oranges.

Chapter 8 • Lesson 1   three hundred eleven **311**

PROFESSIONAL DEVELOPMENT   Math Talk in Action

As children work on Exercise 4, they discuss how they counted.

Teacher:	How many oranges did you count in the circle of oranges?
Rosa:	I counted 20.
James:	I counted 21. I do not think I counted right.
Teacher:	Yes, 20 is correct. How did you count the oranges?
Rosa:	I chose an orange and started counting from there. I put a dot on that orange and every one after that as I counted.
Teacher:	How did you count, James?

James:	I picked an orange to start and counted 1. Then I put a dot on every other orange as I counted.
Zoe:	James, I think you forgot to put a dot when you started counting. It sounds like you started making dots when you counted 2. That means you counted the first one two times.
James:	I think you are right. I will count them again, but will use X's instead of dots so I do not get mixed up.
Teacher:	How many did you count this time, James?
James:	I counted 20. Hurrah!
Teacher:	Good work, class!

PROBLEM SOLVING REAL WORLD

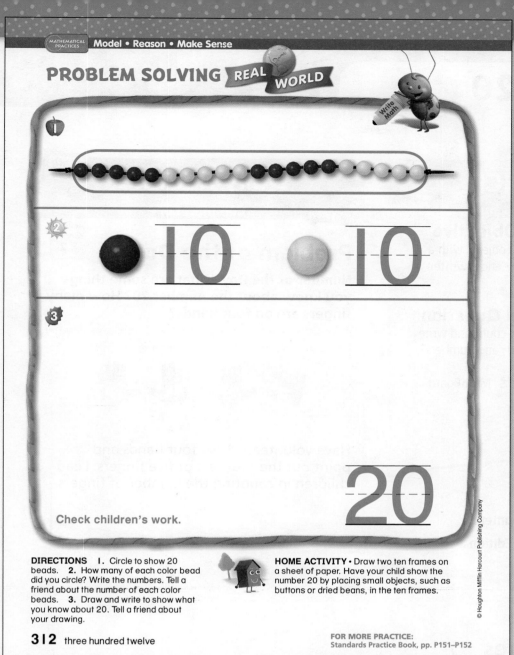

1

2

10

10

3

20

Check children's work.

DIRECTIONS 1. Circle to show 20 beads. **2.** How many of each color bead did you circle? Write the numbers. Tell a friend about the number of each color beads. **3.** Draw and write to show what you know about 20. Tell a friend about your drawing.

HOME ACTIVITY • Draw two ten frames on a sheet of paper. Have your child show the number 20 by placing small objects, such as buttons or dried beans, in the ten frames.

© Houghton Mifflin Harcourt Publishing Company

312 three hundred twelve

FOR MORE PRACTICE:
Standards Practice Book, pp. P151–P152

▶ **Problem Solving** MATHEMATICAL PRACTICES

Read the directions for Exercise 1. Ask children to explain how they will solve the problem.

- **Count the first set of five blue beads and the first set of five yellow beads. How many do you have?** 10

- **How many more beads than 10 do you need to circle to make 20?** 10

Discuss with children how they might know the correct number of beads to circle without counting. Children should realize that the color changes after every five beads and that 2 fives make 10, and four sets of five make 20.

For Exercise 2 have children write how many blue beads and how many yellow beads they circled.

 In Exercise 3 discuss with children ideas for drawing what they know about 20.

- **What will you draw to show what you know about 20?** Responses could include the kind of object and the number 20 possibly made in two sets of 10.

Have children discuss their drawings with a friend.

4 SUMMARIZE MATHEMATICAL PRACTICES

Essential Question

How can you show and count 20 objects? I can use cubes to fill two ten frames to show 20. I can make two ten-cube trains to show 20.

Differentiated Instruction INDEPENDENT ACTIVITIES

Grab-and-Go!

Differentiated Centers Kit

Activities 19 and 20

Children complete the orange Activity Card 20 by showing sets of 19 and 20 objects and labeling how many are in each set.

Literature Where's the Party?

Children read the book and recognize the order of numbers through 20.

Games Sweet and Sour Path

Children increase familiarity with numbers from 1 to 30 with repeated counting forward to move along the game path.

Digital Path

- Animated Math Models
- iT iTools
- MM HMH Mega Math
- Soar to Success Math
- eStudent Edition

Count and Write 20

LESSON AT A GLANCE

Common Core Standard
Know number names and the count sequence.
CC.K.CC.3 Write numbers from 0 to 20. Represent a number of objects with a written numeral 0–20 (with 0 representing a count of no objects).

Also CC.K.CC.4a, CC.K.CC.4b, CC.K.CC.4c, CC.K.CC.5

Lesson Objective
Represent 20 objects with a number name and a written numeral.

Essential Question
How can you count and write 20 with words and numbers?

Materials MathBoard

Digital Path

 **Animated Math Models**

 iT **iTools: Counters**

HMH Mega Math

eStudent Edition

Daily Routines
 Math Board

Common Core

Problem of the Day
 eTransparency 8.2

Number of the Day **What are some things you know about the number 20? How many fingers are on four hands?**

It has 2 tens, it is greater than 19, and it follows 19 when we count. We write it with a 2 and a 0; 20

Have volunteers show four hands and point out the four sets of five fingers. Lead children in counting the number of fingers.

COMMON CORE MATHEMATICAL PRACTICES
Using Ten Frames

Using two ten frames together with cubes or counters to show the number 20 continues the work from the previous chapter. The ten frames clearly show sets of 5 and 10, and when both ten frames are full, children can see 20 cubes or counters. Ten frames allow children to see when a number is greater than 10 or less than 20.

When children first begin using a ten frame, many will count every counter. They may see that each row has five and each ten frame has ten and they can start counting from 5 or 10.

Using a ten frame helps children develop relationships between given numbers and the anchors 5 and 10. Exposure to multiples of 5 and 10 prepares children for work with counting, telling time, and counting coins.

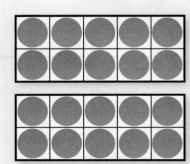

Differentiated Instruction Activities

ELL Language Support Visual / Small Group

Strategy: Define

Materials two-color counters, Numeral Cards (16–23)
(see *eTeacher Resources*)

Children can define words by matching words or visuals to their definitions.

- Put sets of 18, 19, and 20 counters on the table.
- Display the numbers 18, 19, and 20.
- Have children count each set of counters and point to each number that matches the set.
- Next, have children name and write the number.

Repeat this activity with different numbers if time permits.

See ELL Activity Guide for leveled activities.

Enrich Visual / Partners

Materials Ten Frames (see *eTeacher Resources*), two-color counters

Give children 20 counters, two ten frames, and paper.

- Have one partner fill the first ten frame completely and fill the second ten frame with one to nine counters.
- Have the second partner count the counters and write the number to match.
- Then the second partner adds one counter to show one greater, counts the counters, and writes the number to match.
- Have partners switch roles and repeat the activity with different numbers of counters.

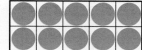 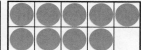

19

RtI Response to Intervention

Reteach Tier 1 Kinesthetic / Whole Class / Small Group

Have children pretend their hands are a ten frame. Have them count their fingers to fill up their "ten frame."

- **How many fingers are on two "ten frames?"** Have children find a friend and wiggle each finger to count from 1 to 20.

You can repeat the activity with toes.

Tier 2 Visual / Kinesthetic / Small Group

Materials Counters and Numerals (1–4), (5–8), (9–12), (13–16), (17–20) (see *eTeacher Resources*)

Give one card to each child. Help children review by matching the counters on the card to each number. Beginning at 1, say the number name and have the child who has that card come to the front and tape his or her card to the board.

- For each number, have all of the children trace the numeral in the air with their finger.
- When all of the cards are in place, have children practice counting from 1 to 20.

COMMON CORE

CC.K.CC.3 Write numbers from 0 to 20. Represent a number of objects with a written numeral 0–20 (with 0 representing a count of no objects).

1 ENGAGE

GO Online · *i*Tools

Materials *i*Tools: Counters

Access Prior Knowledge Use *i*Tools to create a set of 18 objects.

- **How many objects?** 18
- **How many more objects will you need to make a set of 20?** two more
- **Place two more objects. Count to make sure that you have 20.**

Continue with other sets and adding more to make sets of 20.

2 TEACH and TALK

GO Online · Animated Math Models

▶ **Listen and Draw** 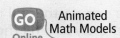 MATHEMATICAL PRACTICES

Read aloud this problem as children listen.

Margo has 20 crayons in her box. Margo wants to write a label with a number and a number word for her crayon box. What will Margo write?

- **How many cubes are in the top row?** 10
  How many cubes are in the bottom row? 10
- **Can you tell how many are in the bottom row without counting? Explain.** Yes. It is just the same as the top row, which has 10, so it also has 10.
- **Count the cubes together. How many cubes are in two rows of 10 cubes?** 20
- **How do we write 20?** I write a 2 and a 0 together.

Help children read the number word *twenty* and name the letters.

- **Trace each number 20 and the number word** *twenty*.
- **Look at the shoes. Count how many shoes.** 20
- **Trace the numbers.**
- **How many shoes are in one pair?** 2
- **How many pairs of shoes make 20?** 10 pairs

Reread the problem.

- **What will Margo write on her label?**
  20, *twenty*

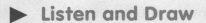

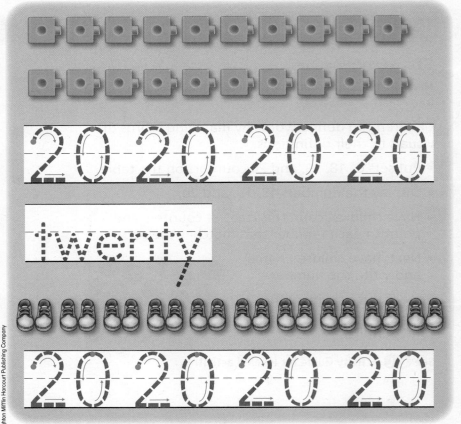

Name _____

Count and Write 20

Essential Question How can you count and write 20 with words and numbers?

COMMON CORE STANDARD CC.K.CC.3
Know number names and the count sequence.

Lesson 8.2

Listen and Draw

DIRECTIONS Count and tell how many cubes. Trace the numbers and the word. Count and tell how many shoes. Trace the numbers.

Check children's work.

Chapter 8 · Lesson 2

three hundred thirteen **313**

© Houghton Mifflin Harcourt Publishing Company

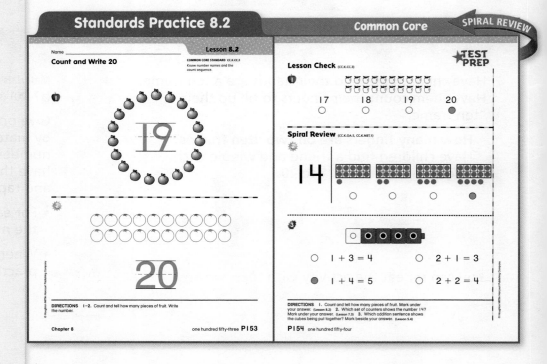

Standards Practice 8.2

Common Core · SPIRAL REVIEW

Name _____

Count and Write 20
COMMON CORE STANDARD CC.K.CC.3
Know number names and the count sequence.

Lesson 8.2

❶ 19

20

DIRECTIONS 1–2. Count and tell how many pieces of fruit. Write the number.

Chapter 8 — one hundred fifty-three **P153**

Lesson Check (CC.K.CC.3)

TEST PREP

❶ 17 18 19 20

Spiral Review (CC.K.OA.5, CC.K.NBT.1)

❷ 14

❸
○ 1 + 3 = 4   ○ 2 + 1 = 3
● 1 + 4 = 5   ○ 2 + 2 = 4

DIRECTIONS 1. Count and tell how many pieces of fruit. Mark under your answer. (Lesson 8.2) 2. Which set of counters shows the number 14? Mark under your answer. (Lesson 7.3) 3. Which addition sentence shows the cubes being put together? Mark beside your answer. (Lesson 5.4)

P154 one hundred fifty-four

Share and Show

Check children's work.

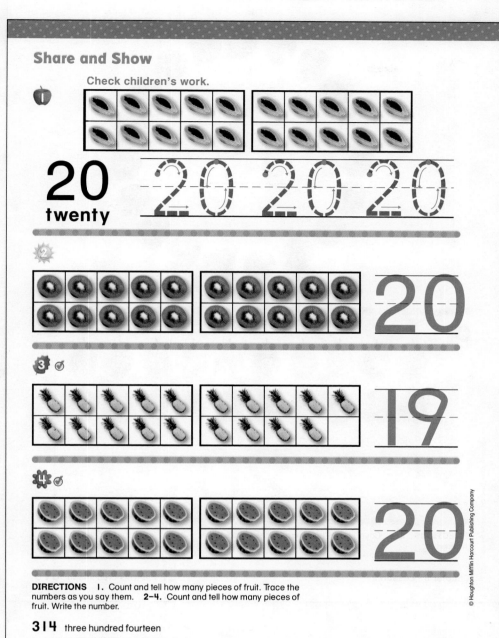

1 20
twenty

20 20 20

2 20

3 19

4 20

DIRECTIONS 1. Count and tell how many pieces of fruit. Trace the numbers as you say them. 2–4. Count and tell how many pieces of fruit. Write the number.

314 three hundred fourteen

© Houghton Mifflin Harcourt Publishing Company

3 PRACTICE

Math Board

▶ **Share and Show** • Guided Practice

- **In Exercise 1, what number and number word do you see?** 20, *twenty*
- **How many pieces of fruit are in the first ten frame?** 10 **How many are in the next ten frame?** 10 **How many are two sets of 10?** 20
- **When you see two filled ten frames, how many objects are there?** 20 **Trace each number 20 and say the number quietly to yourself.**
- **Look at Exercise 2. How many filled ten frames are there?** 2 **If you can, without counting, tell how many kiwi halves there are.** 20 **Write the number.**

Use similar questioning to help children complete Exercises 3 and 4. For Exercise 3, ask children if they had to count to find 9 or if they were able to tell just by seeing one empty space. Remind children that 19 is one less than 20.

Use Exercises 3 and 4 for **Quick Check**.

✓ **Quick Check** RtI

If → a child misses Exercises 3 and 4

Then → **Differentiate Instruction** with
- RtI Tier 1 Activity, p. 313B
- Reteach 8.2
- Soar to Success Math 2.12

Reteach 8.2

RtI

Name _____

Lesson 8.2
Reteach

Count and Write 20

COMMON CORE STANDARD CC.K.CC.3
Know number names and the count sequence.

1 Check children's work.

20
twenty
20 20 20

19

20

DIRECTIONS 1. Count and tell how many counters. Draw a dot on each counter as you count them. Trace the numbers as you say them. 2–3. Count and tell how many pieces of fruit. Touch each fruit as you count. Trace the number.

Reteach
© Houghton Mifflin Harcourt Publishing Company
R62
Grade K

Enrich 8.2

Name _____

Lesson 8.2
Enrich

Count and Match

COMMON CORE STANDARD CC.K.CC.3
Know number names and the count sequence.

1 Check children's work.

20 — nineteen

18 — twenty

20 — twenty

19 — eighteen

DIRECTIONS 1. Count the insects in each group. Write the number. Draw a line to match the insects to the correct number word.

Enrich
© Houghton Mifflin Harcourt Publishing Company
E62
Grade K

⚠ COMMON ERRORS

Error Children may not write the zero in the number 20.

Example Children write 2 instead of 20.

Springboard to Learning Explain that the 2 in 20 stands for two sets of 10. Point out that if you just write 2 with no 0 after it, the number means two, not twenty.

► **More Practice**

- **Look at Exercise 5. Choose an apple to start. Draw a dot on each apple as you count in counting order. The last number word you say tells the number of apples.**
- **How many apples?** 19 **Write the number.**

Have children use a similar process for counting the pears in Exercise 6.

- **How many pears are in the top row?** 10 **How many pears are in the bottom row?** 10 **How many are two sets of 10?** 20 **Write the number.**

H.O.T. Problem In Exercise 5, what if you started counting from a different apple? Would there still be 19 apples? Explain. Possible answer: There would still be 19 apples. It does not matter where you start counting.

Go Deeper

Help children conclude that if objects are placed in a circle, they can begin counting any object. It is important for them to mark the objects so they do not count any twice. Have children explain different ways of counting the rows in Exercise 6.

Name _____

5

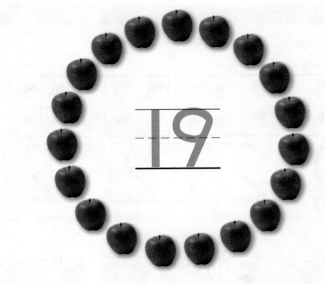

6

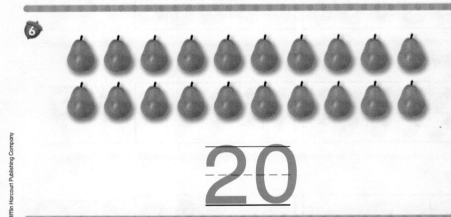

DIRECTIONS **5–6.** Count and tell how many pieces of fruit. Write the number.

Chapter 8 · Lesson 2   three hundred fifteen **315**

Cross-Curricular   **SCIENCE**

Materials lemons

Discuss with children that people can learn about their world using their five senses—sight, sound, taste, smell, and touch.

- **If I want to know whether this lemon is sweet or sour, which sense will I use?** taste
- Continue asking questions about the lemon, such as: **If I want to know how the lemon feels, which sense will I use?** touch
- Then have the children draw 20 lemons that they might see at the market.

SOCIAL STUDIES

Materials play clay

- Talk about what might be seen at an art museum. Explain that some artists make paintings or sculptures to show what people and things are like.
- Discuss how paintings and sculptures of families that lived long ago are different than those of today's families. Talk about the clothing, homes, and toys. Tell children that marbles were used long ago.
- Have children tell about art that they have seen. Explain that they will use clay to show what they know about the number 20 by making marbles and arranging them.
- Give children time to use the clay and then invite them to share their "art" in a class museum.

PROBLEM SOLVING REAL WORLD

1

18

19

20

Check children's work.

2

20

Check children's work.

DIRECTIONS 1. Circle a number. Draw more fruit to show that number. **2.** Draw a set of objects that has a number of objects one greater than 19. Write how many objects are in the set. Tell a friend about your drawing.

HOME ACTIVITY · Have your child use small objects, such as pebbles or pasta pieces, to show the number 20. Then have him or her write the number on a piece of paper.

316 three hundred sixteen

FOR MORE PRACTICE:
Standards Practice Book, pp. P153–P154

© Houghton Mifflin Harcourt Publishing Company

▶ **Problem Solving** (MATHEMATICAL PRACTICES)

For Exercise 1, instruct children to circle any one of the three numbers.

- **Count the pieces of fruit. How many are there?** 10 **Draw more pieces of fruit to match the number you circled.**

For Exercise 2, children will be drawing objects. Talk with them about simple drawings, such as shapes, that they might use.

- **To draw a number of objects one greater than 19, start by drawing 19 objects.**

Encourage children to use sets of 10 for their drawings.

- **Now draw one more. Count how many you have in all and write the number.** 20
- **How many sets of ten did you draw?** 2
- **Tell a friend about your drawing.**

4 SUMMARIZE (MATHEMATICAL PRACTICES)

Essential Question

How can you count and write 20 with words and numbers? I can count from 1 to 20. I can draw two ten-cube trains to show 20. I can show that two filled ten frames show 20. I can write the number 20 and the number word *twenty*. I can write that 10 and 10 more make 20.

Differentiated Instruction — INDEPENDENT ACTIVITIES

Grab-and-Go!
Differentiated Centers Kit

Activities 19 and 20

Children complete the orange Activity Card 20 by showing sets of 19 and 20 objects and labeling how many are in each set.

Literature
Where's the Party?

Children read the book and recognize the order of numbers through 20.

Games
Sweet and Sour Path

Children increase familiarity with numbers from 1 to 30 with repeated counting forward to move along the game path.

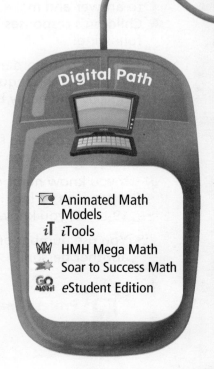

Digital Path

- Animated Math Models
- iT iTools
- HMH Mega Math
- Soar to Success Math
- eStudent Edition

Count and Order to 20

LESSON AT A GLANCE

Common Core Standard
Know number names and the count sequence.
CC.K.CC.2 Count forward beginning from a given number within the known sequence (instead of having to begin at 1).

Also CC.K.CC.4c

Lesson Objective
Count forward to 20 from a given number.

Essential Question
How can you count forward to 20 from a given number?

Materials
MathBoard, connecting cubes

Digital Path

- ☑ Animated Math Models
- ᴹᴹ HMH Mega Math
- iᵀ iTools: Counters
- 🅶🅾 eStudent Edition

COMMON CORE PROFESSIONAL DEVELOPMENT

About the Math

If Children Ask

If a child asks why we put numbers in order, ask the class to answer and make a list of the reasons they can name. Children's responses and yours might sound like the following:

- Knowing the order of numbers can help us count; if you know the sequence of numbers, you can say them quickly and easily because you know what numbers come next.

- You use counting sequences in games, as players count off or as you keep score.

- If you know numbers in order, you can tell which team is winning by looking for the greater score. If a score is 19 to 18, you know that 19 is the greater score.

- You use number order to tell if one person is older than another person.

Professional Development Video Podcasts

Daily Routines

Math Board

Common Core

SPIRAL REVIEW

Problem of the Day

eTransparency **8.3**

Calendar Math What number is just before 15 on the class calendar? What number is just after it?
14; 16

 Have different children point out the numbers 1 to 20 on the calendar and lead the class in saying them.

Fluency Builder

Materials Addition Fact Cards (within 5) (see *eTeacher Resources*), connecting cubes

Add Within 5

Show children the addition fact card for $2 + 2 = \square$.

- **You can use two colors of cubes to model this addition sentence. Make a cube train with two blue cubes and two red cubes.**

- **How many cubes do you have in all?** 4 **What number goes in the box on the card?** 4

Distribute a fact card to each pair. Have them make two-color models to show the equation. Then have them tell how many in all.

- Notice which children are able to count forward to find the number in all.

Differentiated Instruction Activities

ELL Language Support Verbal / Linguistic · Small Group

Strategy: Model Language

Materials connecting cubes

Children can learn correct pronunciation by repeating words and sentences that are modeled by native speakers.

- Put out a set of 11 cubes and a set of 17 cubes.

- Have children repeat the following sentences: **Seventeen is greater than eleven. Eleven is less than seventeen.**

- Give each child 20 connecting cubes. Have children make a set of cubes for any number.

- Compare the children's sets with sentences using the terms *greater than* and *less than*. Have children repeat each sentence.

See **ELL** Activity Guide for leveled activities.

Enrich Visual · Small Group

Materials Numeral Cards (0–7), (8–15), (16–23) (see *eTeacher Resources*)

Select a child to place the cards in order showing 1 to 10 in one row and 11 to 20 in a row below.

- Ask children to point to and read the numbers.

- Turn over a few cards at random and ask which numbers are missing.

- **How can you tell what numbers are missing?** by counting and seeing which numbers that we counted are not there; by knowing what comes before or after the missing numbers

RtI Response to Intervention

Reteach Tier 1 Visual / Kinesthetic · Whole Class / Small Group

Materials Numeral Cards (0–7), (8–15), (16–23) (see *eTeacher Resources*)

Give each child a numeral card, 1 to 20.

- Give clues about each number, such as the following. **This number is greater than 11 and less than 13.**

- Have children with that number stand up and call it out. Have children count forward together from that number to 20.

- Repeat the activity by giving children two consecutive cards.

| 11 | 12 | 13 |

Tier 2 Visual / Kinesthetic · Small Group

Materials Counters and Numerals (1–4), (5–8), (9–12), (13–16), (17–20) (see *eTeacher Resources*)

Distribute one or two cards to each child. Model how to play "I Have, Who Has?"

- For example, hold up the 10 card. **I have 10, who has the number that is one greater?** Have the child with the 11 card hold it up.

- Now it is that child's turn to say "I have 11, who has the number that is one greater?"

- After counting a few cards, pick a different number card to start with and repeat activity.

1 ENGAGE
GO Online *i*Tools

Materials *i*Tools: Counters

Access Prior Knowledge Have children use *i*Tools to create a set of 17 counters and a set of 19 counters.

- **Which set has more counters?** the set of 19
- **Which set has fewer counters?** the set of 17
- **Which number is greater, 19 or 17?** 19
- **Which number is less?** 17

Continue with different sets to 20.

2 TEACH and TALK
GO Online Animated Math Models

▶ **Listen and Draw** MATHEMATICAL PRACTICES

Materials connecting cubes

Read this problem aloud as children listen.

Izzy made cards for 6, 8, 7, and 5. He wanted to show the cards in order. How should he show them?

Have children look at the numbers on the page as they count forward from 1 to 20 together.

- **Choose a number from 1 to 19. Draw a line under it.** Remind children that each number they count is one greater than the one before it.

- **What number is one greater than the one you chose? Circle that number.**

- **What number is one less than the one you chose?** Check children's answers. **How do you know?** Possible answer: When I count, it is the number I say just before I say my number.

- Have children build cube trains to model the number underlined and the one circled. Remind children that the next number name they say when counting refers to a quantity that is one larger.

- **Draw the cube trains and circle the larger cube train.**

Repeat the word problem with children.

- **How should Izzy show his cards?** 5, 6, 7, 8

CC.K.CC.2 Count forward beginning from a given number within the known sequence (instead of having to begin at 1).

Name _____

Count and Order to 20

Essential Question How can you count forward to 20 from a given number?

COMMON CORE STANDARD CC.K.CC.2
Know number names and the count sequence.

Lesson 8.3

Listen and Draw

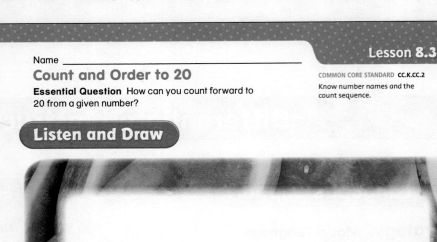

1 2 3 4 5 6 7 8 9 10 11 12 13 14 15 16 17 18 19 20

Check children's work.

DIRECTIONS Draw a line under a number. Count forward to 20 from that number. Use the terms *greater than* and *less than* to compare and describe the order of numbers. Circle the number that is one greater than the number you underlined. Build cube trains to model the numbers you marked. Draw the cube trains. Circle the larger cube train.

Chapter 8 • Lesson 3

three hundred seventeen **317**

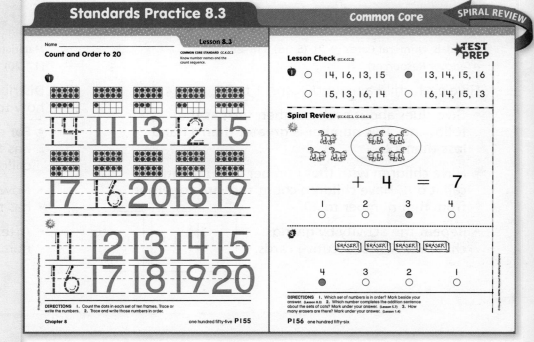

Standards Practice 8.3

Common Core SPIRAL REVIEW

Name _____

Count and Order to 20

COMMON CORE STANDARD CC.K.CC.2
Know number names and the count sequence.

Lesson 8.3

❶ 14, 11, 13, 12, 15

17, 16, 20, 18, 19

11, 12, 13, 14, 15

16, 17, 18, 19, 20

DIRECTIONS 1. Count the dots in each set of ten frames. Trace or write the numbers. 2. Trace and write those numbers in order.

Chapter 8

one hundred fifty-five **P155**

Lesson Check (CC.K.CC.2)

★TEST PREP

❶ ○ 14, 16, 13, 15   ● 13, 14, 15, 16
  ○ 15, 13, 16, 14   ○ 16, 14, 15, 13

Spiral Review (CC.K.CC.3, CC.K.OA.2)

❷ ____ + 4 = 7

  1   2   3   4
  ○   ○   ●   ○

❸ [ERASER] [ERASER] [ERASER] [ERASER]

  4   3   2   1
  ●   ○   ○   ○

DIRECTIONS 1. Which set of numbers is in order? Mark beside your answer. (Lesson 8.3) 2. Which number completes the addition sentence about the sets of cats? Mark under your answer. (Lesson 5.7) 3. How many erasers are there? Mark under your answer. (Lesson 1.4)

P156 one hundred fifty-six

Share and Show

1 2 3 4 5 6 7 8 9 10 11 12 13 14 15 16 17 18 19 20

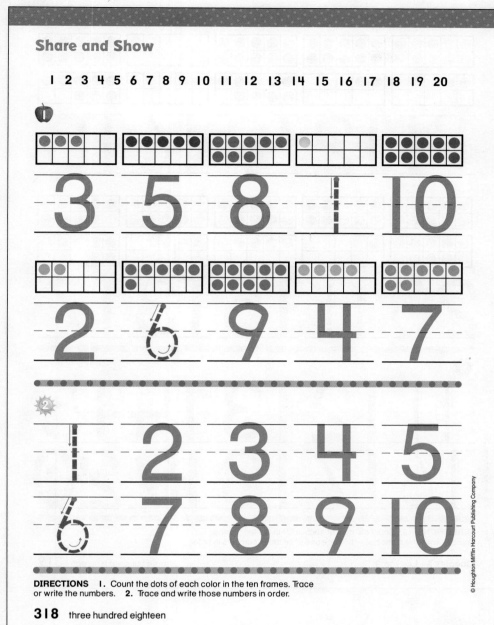

DIRECTIONS 1. Count the dots of each color in the ten frames. Trace or write the numbers. 2. Trace and write those numbers in order.

318 three hundred eighteen

---

3 PRACTICE Math Board

▶ **Share and Show • Guided Practice**

With children, read the numbers 1 to 20. Then direct attention to Exercise 1.

- **How many red counters are there in the first ten frame?** 3 **Write the number.**
- **The next frame has the top row filled. Do you know how many without counting?** Yes. 5 **Write the number.**

Ask similar questions for the rest of the ten frames. Children will trace the numbers 1 and 6 and write the others.

For Exercise 2, tell children that they will write the numbers from Exercise 1 in counting order.

- **Of the numbers you see, which one comes first?** 1 **Trace the number.**

Have children complete the exercise by writing the numbers from 1 to 10 in order.

- **How did you know what numbers to write after the 6 on the second line?** I counted forward from 6 to 10.

Have volunteers take turns sharing what they wrote.

Reteach 8.3 RtI

Name _____

Lesson 8.3
Reteach

Count and Order to 20

COMMON CORE STANDARD CC.K.CC.2
Know number names and the count sequence.

DIRECTIONS 1. Count the dots in each set of ten frames. Trace the numbers. Then point to each number as you count in order from 10. 2. Write the number that comes after 15.
Reteach
© Houghton Mifflin Harcourt Publishing Company
R63
Grade K

Enrich 8.3

Name _____

Lesson 8.3
Enrich

Count Marbles

COMMON CORE STANDARD CC.K.CC.2
Know number names and the count sequence.

DIRECTIONS 1. Count the marbles. Write the number of marbles in each set. 2. Write the numbers in order.
Enrich
© Houghton Mifflin Harcourt Publishing Company
E63
Grade K

⚠ COMMON ERRORS

Error Children may have trouble counting forward from a given number.

Example Children write the incorrect number after the number 6 in Exercise 2.

Springboard to Learning Have children write numbers on self-stick notes and place them in order in small sets such as 6 to 10, as they count forward aloud.

► More Practice

Call attention to Exercise 3. Have children complete the exercise by counting the counters or by using other strategies and then tracing or writing the number that tells how many.

Have children complete Exercise 4 by tracing and writing the numbers from 11 to 20 in order. Then invite children to read the numbers in order.

Use Exercise 3 for **Quick Check**.

 Quick Check

If → a child misses Exercise 3

Then → **Differentiate Instruction** with
- RtI Tier 1 Activity, p. 317B
- Reteach 8.3
- Soar to Success Math 7.13

H.O.T. Problem Can you describe the same number using both the terms *greater than* and *less than*? If so, give an example. Yes. Possible answer: 2 is greater than 1 and 2 is less than 3.

Go Deeper MATHEMATICAL PRACTICES

Discuss the relationship of numbers and how a number can, at the same time, be greater than one number and less than another.

- **What number is one greater than 12?** 13
- **What number is two less than 15?** 13

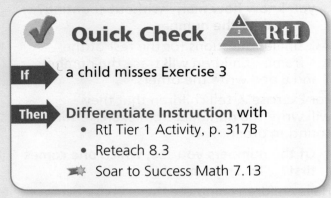

Name _____

DIRECTIONS 3. Count the dots of each color in the ten frames. Trace or write the numbers. 4. Trace and write those numbers in order.

Chapter 8 • Lesson 3

three hundred nineteen **319**

PROBLEM SOLVING REAL WORLD

1	2	3	4	5
6	7	8	9	10
11	12	13	14	15
16	17	18	19	20

DIRECTIONS Write to show the numbers in order. Count forward to 20 from one of the numbers you wrote.

HOME ACTIVITY · Give your child a set of 11 objects, a set of 12 objects, and a set of 13 objects. Have him or her count the objects in each set and place the sets in numerical order.

FOR MORE PRACTICE:
Standards Practice Book, pp. P155–P156

320 three hundred twenty

▶ **Problem Solving** MATHEMATICAL PRACTICES

• **Look at this page. What do you see?** a number chart

• **What do you notice about this number chart?** The numbers are in order.

• **Write the numbers in order on the number chart.**

• **Point to one of the numbers you wrote. Count forward from that number to 20.**

 Tell children to write to show what they know about the missing numbers.

• **Now count the numbers on the chart in order.** 1, 2, 3…, 18, 19, 20,

Have children share how they found the missing numbers.

4 SUMMARIZE MATHEMATICAL PRACTICES

Essential Question

How can you count forward to 20 from a given number? I can start at any number and count forward by ones until I get to 20.

 **Differentiated Instruction** INDEPENDENT ACTIVITIES

Grab-and-Go!
Differentiated Centers Kit

Activities
Place Your Order

Children complete the purple Activity Card 20 by identifying the numbers 10 through 20.

Literature
Summertime Math!

Children read the book and count and compare objects up to 15.

Games
Sweet and Sour Path

Children increase familiarity with numbers from 1 to 30 with repeated counting forward to move along the game path.

 Digital Path

- 📺 Animated Math Models
- iT iTools
- MM HMH Mega Math
- ⭐ Soar to Success Math
- GO eStudent Edition

Problem Solving • Compare Numbers to 20

LESSON AT A GLANCE

Common Core Standard
Compare numbers.
CC.K.CC.6 Identify whether the number of objects in one group is greater than, less than, or equal to the number of objects in another group, e.g., by using matching and counting strategies.

Also CC.K.CC.3

Lesson Objective
Solve problems by using the strategy *make a model.*

Essential Question
How can you solve problems using the strategy *make a model*?

Materials
MathBoard, connecting cubes

Digital Path

- 🖥 **Animated Math Models**
- 👑 **HMH Mega Math**
- iᵀ **iTools: Counters**
- 🎒 **eStudent Edition**

PROFESSIONAL DEVELOPMENT COMMON CORE

About the Math

Why Teach This

In this lesson and others, numbers are represented in a variety of ways. This not only enhances children's understanding, it also shows that a single idea may have many different representations.

Manipulatives such as connecting cubes are used to model numbers in concrete ways. In this lesson, children use connecting cubes to help them identify whether the number of objects in one set is greater than, less than, or equal to the number of objects in another set. Because the connecting cubes are sensory—they can be seen, handled, and moved about—they attract and hold children's attention. Modeling with manipulatives helps children visualize quantities and compare and contrast numbers.

🎧 **PODCASTING** **Professional Development Video Podcasts**

Problem of the Day

eTransparency **8.4**

Words of the Day How can we compare the number of cubes by using *less than* and *greater than*?

4 is less than 8 and 8 is greater than 4

Show children cubes as pictured and have them compare. Then show a set of 6 cubes and have a child display a set of cubes with the same number.

Fluency Builder

Counting Tape

EVERY DAY COUNTS®

Materials Counting Tape

Continue to update daily. As numbers on the Counting Tape go beyond 100, explain that 100 and 1 left over is 101. Discuss numbers that appear on the following days in the same way. It won't be long before many see a familiar pattern unfolding in the numbers above 100.

Continue to discuss the numbers that appeared earlier as well. For example, challenge children to identify a "mystery number." Cover up a number with a blank square and ask children to "guess" the hidden number and convince the class of their decision. (I know the mystery number is 52 because it comes right after 51.)

| 90 | 91 | 92 | 93 | 94 |

| 100 | 101 | 102 | 103 | 104 |

Differentiated Instruction Activities

ELL Language Support Auditory / Visual / Small Group

Strategy: Restate

Materials classroom objects

Restate key vocabulary by renaming terms in a more familiar way.

- Show children two sets of objects (19, 20).

- Explain that when you compare numbers you talk about *greater than* or *less than*. When you compare objects you talk about *more* or *fewer*.

- Have children count the objects. Explain that the set of 20 objects has one more than the set of 19.

Continue to show children sets of objects. Have them tell which has more or fewer objects and how much greater than or less than the other each number of objects is.

See **ELL** Activity Guide for leveled activities.

Enrich Visual / Partners

Materials red circle stickers, chart paper, Numeral Cards (0–7), (8–15), (16–23) (see *eTeacher Resources*)

Draw four large trees on chart paper. Place 1 to 20 stickers on each tree.

- Have children work with a partner. Have each partner choose two trees, count the apples on each tree, and find the matching numeral cards. The partners compare the four numbers in as many ways as they can, using *greater than* and *less than*.

RtI Response to Intervention

Reteach Tier 1 Kinesthetic / Visual / Whole Class / Small Group

Materials construction paper, fruit and vegetable stickers, Numeral Cards (0–7), (8–15), (16–23) (see *eTeacher Resources*)

Prepare pictures of baskets of fruit (or vegetables) to show numbers 3 to 18. Provide each child with a picture.

- Each child counts the number of objects in his or her basket and finds the matching card.

- Have each child turn to a partner and compare the numbers by using *greater than* and *less than*.

- Then have partners identify and describe numbers that are one greater than, one less than, two greater than, and two less than their numbers.

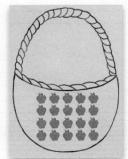

Tier 2 Kinesthetic / Visual / Verbal / Small Group

Materials Workmat 4 (ten frames) (see *eTeacher Resources*), two-color counters

Give each child a handful of counters. Have children count out the counters onto Workmat 4.

- Each child should turn to a partner, compare workmats, and describe who has more counters.

- Have a volunteer tell the group how many counters he or she has. **I have 12 counters. Who has more than 12 counters?**

- Children take turns responding, "I have more than 12 counters. I have [number] counters, which is _____ more."

Repeat until each child has had a turn.

1 ENGAGE GO Online iTools

Materials *iTools:* Counters

Access Prior Knowledge For more practice with counting sets, show a set of 10 counters and a set of seven counters.

Have children describe the sets using the terms *10 and 7 more.* Continue with sets of 18, 19, and 20.

2 TEACH and TALK GO Online Animated Math Models

▶ Unlock the Problem MATHEMATICAL PRACTICES

Materials connecting cubes

Read aloud this problem as children listen.

Alison has a number of yellow cubes one greater than 15. Josh has a number of green cubes one less than 17. Who has more cubes?

Have partners use cubes to work through the problem. Ask each pair to decide what they need to find out first.

- **The problem says that Alison has a number of yellow cubes one greater than 15. How many yellow cubes should you start with for Alison?** 15 **Use cubes to show this as ten ones and some more ones. Add one more. How many does Alison have now?** 16

- **How many green cubes does Josh have?** one less than 17 **Start with 17 green cubes. Use cubes to show this as ten ones and some more ones. Now what should you do?** Take 1 away. **How many does Josh have now?** 16

Explain that there are two ways to compare the cube trains, matching the cubes and counting the cubes. Have children decide which strategy they will use. Explain to children that the ten-cube trains are the same so they will be comparing the more ones.

- **Who has more cubes?** Neither; they have the same number of cubes.

- **Explain how you compared the sets.** Answers should describe either matching the cubes or counting the cubes.

Have children draw the sets and tell about their drawings.

- **Tell a friend about your drawing.**

COMMON CORE **CC.K.CC.6** Identify whether the number of objects in one group is greater than, less than, or equal to the number of objects in another group, e.g., by using matching and counting strategies.

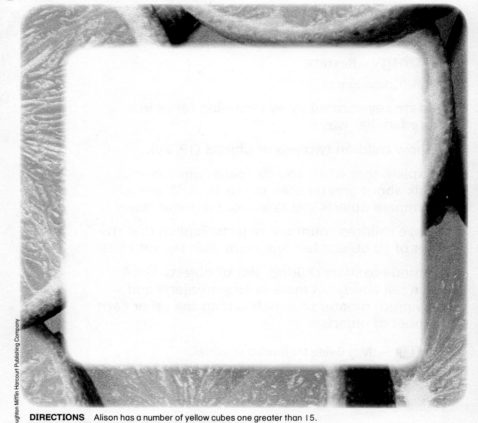

Name _____

Problem Solving • Compare Numbers to 20

PROBLEM SOLVING
Lesson 8.4

Essential Question How can you solve problems using the strategy *make a model?*

COMMON CORE STANDARD **CC.K.CC.6**
Compare numbers.

🔑 Unlock the Problem

DIRECTIONS Alison has a number of yellow cubes one greater than 15. Josh has a number of green cubes one less than 17. Show the cubes. Compare the sets of cubes. Draw the cubes. Tell a friend about your drawing. **Check children's work.**

Chapter 8 • Lesson 4   three hundred twenty-one **321**

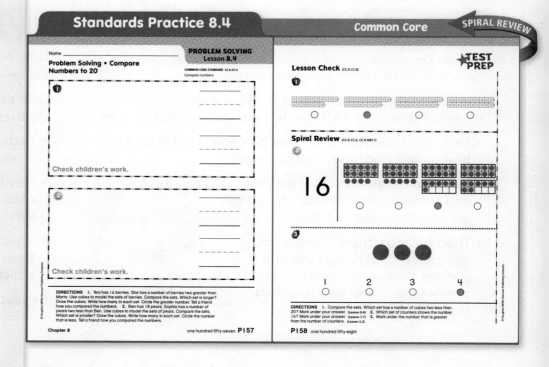

Standards Practice 8.4   Common Core   SPIRAL REVIEW

Name _____

Problem Solving • Compare Numbers to 20

PROBLEM SOLVING
Lesson 8.4

COMMON CORE STANDARD CC.K.CC.6
Compare numbers.

①

Check children's work.

✹

Check children's work.

DIRECTIONS 1. Teni has 16 berries. She has a number of berries two greater than Marta. Use cubes to model the sets of berries. Compare the sets. Which set is larger? Draw the cubes. Write how many in each set. Circle the greater number. Tell a friend how you compared the numbers. 2. Ben has 18 pears. Sophia has a number of pears two less than Ben. Use cubes to model the sets of pears. Compare the sets. Which set is smaller? Draw the cubes. Write how many in each set. Circle the number that is less. Tell a friend how you compared the numbers.

Chapter 8   one hundred fifty-seven **P157**

Lesson Check (CC.K.CC.6)

★TEST PREP

①

Spiral Review (CC.K.CC.4, CC.K.NBT.1)

✹

16

③

    1   2   3   4

DIRECTIONS 1. Compare the sets. Which set has a number of cubes two less than 20? Mark under your answer. (Lesson 8.4) 2. Which set of counters shows the number 16? Mark under your answer. (Lesson 8.4) 3. Mark under the number that is greater than the number of counters. (Lesson 2.2)

P158 one hundred fifty-eight

Try Another Problem

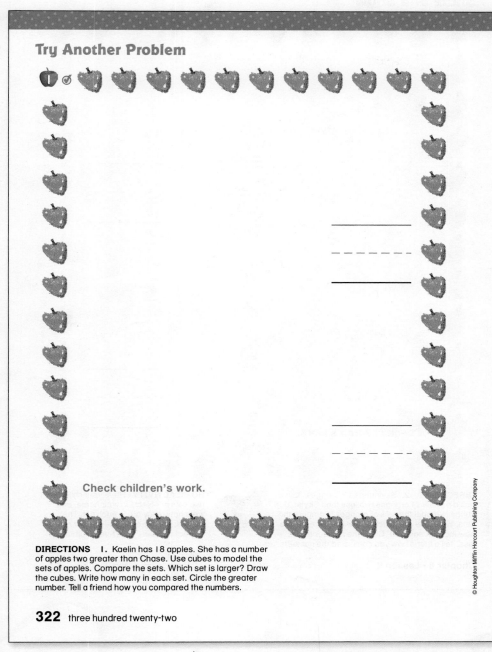

DIRECTIONS 1. Kaelin has 18 apples. She has a number of apples two greater than Chase. Use cubes to model the sets of apples. Compare the sets. Which set is larger? Draw the cubes. Write how many in each set. Circle the greater number. Tell a friend how you compared the numbers.

Check children's work.

© Houghton Mifflin Harcourt Publishing Company

322 three hundred twenty-two

▶ **Try Another Problem**

For Exercise 1, read the problem and ask children what they need to find out first. *how many apples Kaelin has*

- **How many apples does Kaelin have?** 18
- **What do you need to find out next?** *how many apples Chase has*
- **Kaelin has a number of apples two greater than Chase. So how many apples does Chase have?** 16

Have children use cubes to model the apples and compare the cubes.

- **Draw the cubes. Write the numbers.**
- **How many in each set?** 18 and 16

Clarify for children that the question "Which set is larger?" means "Which set has more."

- **Which set is larger?** 18 **How do you know?** *It has more cubes.*
- **Which number is greater?** 18

Have children circle the greater number.

- **Tell a friend how you compared the numbers.**

Use Exercise 1 for **Quick Check.**

✓ Quick Check

If → a child misses Exercise 1

Then → **Differentiate Instruction** with
- RtI Tier 1 Activity, p. 321B
- Reteach 8.4
- Soar to Success Math 70.01

⚠ COMMON ERRORS

Error Children may not be able to identify the greater number.

Example Children identify the number 16 as greater than 18.

Springboard to Learning Model 18 and 16 with counters using matching. Help children see that there are two counters without a match, so 18 is greater than 16.

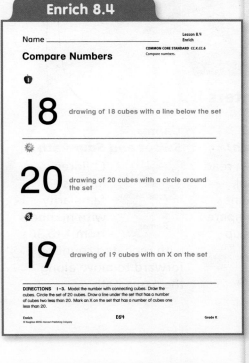

Reteach 8.4 ▲ RtI

Name _____

**Problem Solving •
Compare Numbers to 20**

Lesson 8.4
Reteach
COMMON CORE STANDARD CC.K.CC.6
Compare numbers.

(19)

17

DIRECTIONS Use cubes to model the sets. 1. Dana has 19 cubes. Trace the cubes. Write the number. 2. Dana has a number of cubes two greater than Ethan. Trace the cubes. Write the number. Compare the sets of cubes in Exercises 1 and 2. Circle the greater number.

Reteach
© Houghton Mifflin Harcourt Publishing Company
R64
Grade K

Enrich 8.4

Name _____

Compare Numbers

Lesson 8.4
Enrich
COMMON CORE STANDARD CC.K.CC.6
Compare numbers.

❶ 18 — drawing of 18 cubes with a line below the set

❷ 20 — drawing of 20 cubes with a circle around the set

❸ 19 — drawing of 19 cubes with an X on the set

DIRECTIONS 1–3. Model the number with connecting cubes. Draw the cubes. 1. Circle the set of 20 cubes. Draw a line under the set that has a number of cubes two less than 20. Mark an X on the set that has a number of cubes one less than 20.

Enrich
© Houghton Mifflin Harcourt Publishing Company
E64
Grade K

③ PRACTICE

▶ **Share and Show** • **Guided Practice**

Read the problem and have children use cubes to model Skyler's and Taylor's sets of oranges.

- **How can you find out which set has fewer cubes?** Possible answers: I can match the cubes to see which set has fewer cubes; I can count how many are in each set of cubes.

- **Have children draw the cubes and write the numbers.**

- **Circle the number that is less. Talk to a friend about how you compared the numbers.**

H.O.T. Problem Have children use cubes to model the following problem: Keiko has three fewer than 20 cubes. Trent has two more cubes that Keiko. How many cubes do they each have? Keiko 17, Trent 19 **Which number is less?** 17

Go Deeper

How did you know which number was less? Possible answer: I know that numbers that come earlier in the counting sequence are less than numbers that come later.

④ SUMMARIZE

Essential Question

How can you solve problems using the strategy *make a model*? I can make a model so that I can match or count objects to solve the problem.

Name _____

Share and Show

Check children's work.

DIRECTIONS 2. Skyler has 19 oranges. Taylor has a number of oranges two less than Skyler. Use cubes to model the sets of oranges. Compare the sets. Which set is smaller? Draw the cubes. Write how many in each set. Circle the number that is less. Tell a friend how you compared the numbers.

 **HOME ACTIVITY** • Have your child count two sets of objects in your home, and write how many are in each set. Then have him or her circle the greater number. Repeat with sets of different numbers.

FOR EXTRA PRACTICE: Standards Practice Book, p. P167

FOR MORE PRACTICE: Standards Practice Book, pp. P157–P158

Chapter 8 • Lesson 4

three hundred twenty-three **323**

© Houghton Mifflin Harcourt Publishing Company

Differentiated Instruction **INDEPENDENT ACTIVITIES**

Grab-and-Go!

Differentiated Centers Kit

Activities
Place Your Order

 Children complete the purple Activity Card 20 by identifying the numbers 10 through 20.

Literature
Summertime Math!

 Children read the book and count and compare objects up to 15.

Games
Sweet and Sour Path

 Children increase familiarity with numbers from 1 to 30 with repeated counting forward to move along the game path.

Digital Path

- 🖥 Animated Math Models
- *i*T *i*Tools
- 𝕄𝕄 HMH Mega Math
- ✹ Soar to Success Math
- GO *e*Student Edition

✓ Mid-Chapter Checkpoint

Concepts and Skills

1 20

2 18 ⟨17⟩

3 ⟨16⟩ 15

★ **Test Prep**

4   17   18   19   **20**
       ○   ○   ○   ●

© Houghton Mifflin Harcourt Publishing Company

DIRECTIONS 1. Count and tell how many. Write the number. (CC.K.CC.3)
2. Write how many pieces of fruit are in each picture. Circle the number that is less. (CC.K.CC.6) **3.** Write how many pieces of fruit are in each picture. Circle the number that is greater. (CC.K.CC.6) **4.** Mark under the number that shows how many pieces of fruit are at the beginning of the row. (CC.K.CC.3)

324 three hundred twenty-four

Formative Assessment

Use the **Mid-Chapter Checkpoint** to assess children's learning and progress in the first half of the chapter. The formative assessment provides the opportunity to adjust teaching methods for individual or whole class instruction.

✓ Data-Driven Decision Making 🔺 RtI

Based on the results of the Mid-Chapter Checkpoint, use the following resources to strengthen individual or whole class instruction.

Item	Lesson	*CCSS	Common Error	Intervene With	Soar to Success Math
1	8.2	CC.K.CC.3	May have difficulty writing the number	R—8.2; TE—p. 313B	2.12
2	8.4	CC.K.CC.6	May have difficulty identifying which number is less	R—8.4; TE—p. 321B	70.01
3	8.4	CC.K.CC.6	May have difficulty identifying which number is greater	R—8.4; TE—p. 321B	70.01
4	8.2	CC.K.CC.3	May miscount the objects	R—8.2; TE—p. 313B	2.12

*CCSS—Common Core State Standards   **Key: R—Reteach Book; TE—RtI Activities**

Count to 50 by Ones

LESSON AT A GLANCE

Common Core Standard
Know number names and the count sequence.
CC.K.CC.1 Count to 100 by ones and by tens.

Also CC.K.CC.2

Lesson Objective
Know the count sequence when counting to 50 by ones.

Essential Question
How does the order of numbers help you to count to 50 by ones?

Vocabulary **fifty**

Materials MathBoard

Digital Path

GO Math! eStudent Edition

COMMON CORE PROFESSIONAL DEVELOPMENT

Building Mathematical Practices

CC.K–12.MB.5 Use appropriate tools strategically.

The use of fifty and hundred charts enhances mathematical knowledge for young children. In this lesson, children are introduced to a fifty chart. Why use a fifty chart instead of manipulatives or a hundred chart to develop counting skills?

On a fifty chart, children can see at a glance which number follows another. They begin to detect patterns in numbers not as obvious when using manipulatives such as connecting cubes or two-color counters. The fifty chart is a different way to look at numbers 1 to 50. Ask children questions such as the following as they study the fifty chart:

- **What do you notice about the numbers in this column of the fifty chart?**

- **How are the numbers in this row like the ones in the next row?**

The fifty chart prepares children for using the hundred chart, a very important tool in the development of place-value concepts.

Daily Routines

Common Core

SPIRAL REVIEW

Problem of the Day

eTransparency 8.5

Number of the Day What number is two greater than 18? What number is two less than 30?
20; 28

Have children start counting at 20 and count forward to 28.

Fluency Builder

Subtract within 5

Materials Subtraction Fact Cards (within 5) (see *eTeacher Resources*), connecting cubes

Show children the subtraction fact card for $5 - 2 = \boxed{}$.

- **You can use connecting cubes to model this number sentence. How many cubes will you start with?** 5 **Why?** That is the number in all.

- **Now take apart the set by the number that is shown after the minus symbol. What is that number?** 2

- **Count to find how many are left, 1, 2, 3.**

- **What number goes in the box on the card?** 3

Literature

From the Grab-and-Go™ Differentiated Centers Kit

Children read the book and count fruit and vegetables up to 30.

Counting at the Market

Differentiated Instruction Activities

ELL Language Support Kinesthetic Partners

Strategy: Identify Patterns

Materials Counters and Numerals (21–24), (25–28), (29–30) (see *eTeacher Resources*)

Children can use patterns to better understand counting.

- Have children help you place the cards in order.
- Encourage children to look for patterns. **How do you know this card comes next?** Possible answer: It has one more counter on it.
- Have children count the cards in order.
- When all of the cards are in order, remove several. Give the cards to a child. Have the child place them back in order.

Continue removing cards for children to place in order.

See **ELL** Activity Guide for leveled activities.

Enrich Kinesthetic Individuals / Partners

Materials Fifty Chart (see *eTeacher Resources*)

Have one partner hold the fifty chart so the other partner cannot see it.

- The partner looking at the fifty chart asks two questions, one at a time, about the numbers on the chart. Sample questions: **What number is one greater than 39?** 40 **What number is greater than 24 and less than 26?** 25
- The partner facing away from the chart answers. Partners switch roles and continue the activity.

1	2	3	4	5	6	7	8	9	10
11	12	13	14	15	16	17	18	19	20
21	22	23	24	25	26	27	28	29	30
31	32	33	34	35	36	37	38	39	40
41	42	43	44	45	46	47	48	49	50

RtI Response to Intervention

Reteach Tier 1 Kinesthetic / Visual Whole Class / Small Group

Materials 10 × 10 Grid (see *eTeacher Resources*)

Use a grid to make a fifty chart with some numbers missing. Write the numbers for 30 squares and leave the other squares blank. Do not leave more than four blank squares in each row.

- Have children point to the first empty box. Count aloud with children to that number.
- Have a child write the missing number.
- Continue counting. Have children take turns writing numbers until the chart is complete.

1	2	3	[ ]	5	[ ]	7	[ ]	[ ]	10
11	[ ]	[ ]	14	15	16	[ ]	18	[ ]	20
[ ]	22	23	[ ]	25	[ ]	27	28	29	[ ]
31	[ ]	33	34	[ ]	[ ]	37	[ ]	39	40
[ ]	42	[ ]	44	45	46	47	[ ]	49	[ ]

Tier 2 Visual / Kinesthetic Small Group

Materials Fifty Chart (see *eTeacher Resources*), crayons

Display a fifty chart to children. Have children count aloud from 1 to 10 as you touch each number.

- Distribute fifty charts and have children count from 1 to 10, pointing to each number. When they get to 10, have children color in the box.
- **When you get to the end of a row, move your finger to the start of the next row to continue counting.** Demonstrate counting 10, 11 by moving your finger to the beginning of the next row.
- Have children repeat the activity for each row until they reach 50. Make sure children point and touch as they count. Have them use a different color crayon for each row.

1 ENGAGE

Access Prior Knowledge Give children more practice comparing numbers. Have them count from 1 to 20.

- **What number is *one greater than 14 and one less than* 16?** 15

Continue with other numbers.

2 TEACH and TALK

▶ **Listen and Draw**

Read the problem aloud as children look at the fifty chart on the page.

Bella wants to count to 50 by reading a fifty chart. Where will she look for the first number? What number will be the last one she says?

- **Why do you think this chart is called a fifty chart?** It shows numbers 1 to 50.
- **How many rows does it have?** 5
- **How many numbers are in each row?** 10
- **What is the first number in the top row?** 1
- **Where should Bella look for the first number?** She should look at the first number in the top row.
- **How are the numbers in the second row like the numbers in the first row?** They are the same numbers, except they have a 1 in front of each number.

Review with children that when they count, each number is one greater than the number before it.

- **Point to each number in the top row. Say the number names in order.** 1, 2, 3, 4, 5, 6, 7, 8, 9, 10
- **Point to the beginning of the next row. What number do you count after 10?** 11

Have children continue to count in order to 20, pointing to each number as they count.

Reread the word problem.

- **What is the last number on the fifty chart?** 50
- **What number will be the last one Bella says?** 50

COMMON CORE **CC.K.CC.1** Count to 100 by ones and by tens.

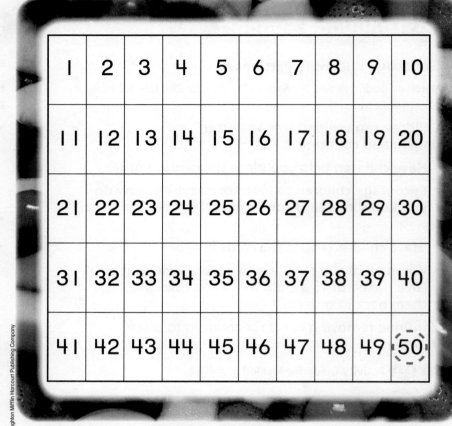

Name _____

Count to 50 by Ones

Essential Question How does the order of numbers help you count to 50 by ones?

Lesson 8.5

COMMON CORE STANDARD CC.K.CC.1
Know number names and the count sequence.

Listen and Draw

1	2	3	4	5	6	7	8	9	10
11	12	13	14	15	16	17	18	19	20
21	22	23	24	25	26	27	28	29	30
31	32	33	34	35	36	37	38	39	40
41	42	43	44	45	46	47	48	49	50

© Houghton Mifflin Harcourt Publishing Company

DIRECTIONS Point to each number as you count to 50. Trace the circle around the number 50.

Check children's work.

Chapter 8 • Lesson 5

three hundred twenty-five **325**

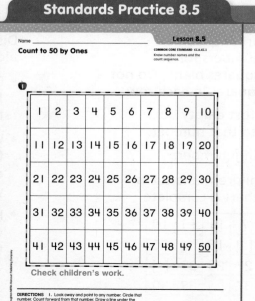

Standards Practice 8.5

Common Core

SPIRAL REVIEW

Name _____

Count to 50 by Ones

COMMON CORE STANDARD CC.K.CC.1
Know number names and the count sequence.

Lesson 8.5

❶

1	2	3	4	5	6	7	8	9	10
11	12	13	14	15	16	17	18	19	20
21	22	23	24	25	26	27	28	29	30
31	32	33	34	35	36	37	38	39	40
41	42	43	44	45	46	47	48	49	50

Check children's work.

© Houghton Mifflin Harcourt Publishing Company

DIRECTIONS 1. Look away and point to any number. Circle that number. Count forward from that number. Draw a line under the number 50.

Chapter 8

one hundred fifty-nine **P159**

Lesson Check (CC.K.CC.1)

★ TEST PREP

❶

1	2	3	4	5	6	7	8	9	10
11	12	13	14	15	16	17	18	19	20
21	22	23	24	25	26	27	28	29	30

20 ○   21 ●   22 ○   23 ○

Spiral Review (CC.K.OA.1, CC.K.OA.3)

❷ ○○ ○ ○ ○ ○ ○ ○

$6 = 5 + 1$ ○ | $5 = 2 + 3$ ○ | $6 = 2 + 4$ ● | $7 = 2 + 5$ ○

❸ ●●●●● ●○○○○ $10 - 3$

5 ○   6 ○   7 ●   8 ○

DIRECTIONS 1. Begin with 1 and count forward to 20. What is the next number? Mark under your answer. (Lesson 8.5) 2. Which addition sentence shows a numbers pair that matches the cube train? Mark under your answer. (Lesson 5.9) 3. Shelley has 10 counters. Three of her counters are white. The rest of her counters are gray. How many are gray? Mark under your answer. (Lesson 6.2)

P160 one hundred sixty

© Houghton Mifflin Harcourt Publishing Company

Share and Show

1	2	3	4	5	6	7	8	9	10
11	12	13	14	(15)	16	17	18	19	20
21	22	23	24	25	26	27	28	29	30
31	32	33	34	35	36	37	38	39	40
41	42	43	44	45	46	47	48	49	50

DIRECTIONS 1. Point to each number as you count to 50. Circle the number 15. Begin with 15 and count forward to 50. Draw a line under the number 50.

326 three hundred twenty-six

© Houghton Mifflin Harcourt Publishing Company

▶ **Share and Show • Guided Practice**

Have children describe the chart on the page.

• **How are the numbers shown on the chart?**
They are shown in order, 1 to 50.

Have children point to each number as you count together. 1, 2, 3, ... 48, 49, 50

Remind children that when they finish counting a row, they move down to the next row and start counting from left to right.

• **Find the number 15. Circle it.**

• **Begin at 15 and count forward to 50.**

• **Draw a line below the number 50.**

COMMON ERRORS

Error Children may not be able to follow the order of the numbers on the chart.

Example Children do not find the number following 10 on the chart.

Springboard to Learning Have children cover all except the top two rows. Count from 1 to 10 and direct attention to the next row. Have children sweep their fingers to the beginning of the second row to continue counting from 11.

▲ RtI

Reteach 8.5

Name _____

Count to 50 by Ones

Lesson 8.5 Reteach

COMMON CORE STANDARD CC.K.CC.1
Know number names and the count sequence.

1 Check children's work.

1	2	3	4	5	6	7	8	9	10
11	12	13	14	15	16	17	18	19	20
21	22	23	24	25	26	27	28	29	30
31	32	33	34	35	36	37	38	39	40
41	42	43	44	45	46	47	48	49	50

DIRECTIONS 1. Count forward from 1. Draw a dot on each number as you count. Begin with 47 and count forward to 50. Color those numbers yellow.

Reteach
© Houghton Mifflin Harcourt Publishing Company

R65

Grade K

Enrich 8.5

Name _____

Complete the Fifty Chart

Lesson 8.5 Enrich

COMMON CORE STANDARD CC.K.CC.1
Know number names and the count sequence.

1

1	2	3	4	5	6	7	8	9	10
11	12	13	14	15	16	17	18	19	20
(21)	22	23	24	25	26	27	28	29	30
31	32	33	34	35	36	37	38	39	40
41	42	43	44	45	46	47	48	49	50

Check children's work.

DIRECTIONS 1. Point to each number as you count to 50. Tell the missing numbers. Find the number that is greater than 20 and less than 22. Circle the number. Find the number that is greater than 29 and less than 31. Draw a line under the number.

Enrich
© Houghton Mifflin Harcourt Publishing Company

E65

Grade K

► More Practice

Call attention to the fifty chart. Count from 1 to 50 as a group. Remind children to point to each number as they count.

Have each child look away from the page and point to any number. Have children circle the number and count forward from that number to 50. They draw a line under the number 50.

H.O.T. Problem John counts forward from 25 to 39. Michele then counts forward to 50. What numbers does Michele say? 40, 41, 42, 43, 44, 45, 46, 47, 48, 49, 50

Go Deeper

Children should be able to use what they know about counting to 50 to continue the counting pattern. Ask how they know what numbers follow 39 to end at 50.

Use Exercise 2 for **Quick Check.**

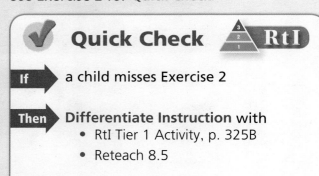
Quick Check

If	a child misses Exercise 2
Then	**Differentiate Instruction** with • RtI Tier 1 Activity, p. 325B • Reteach 8.5

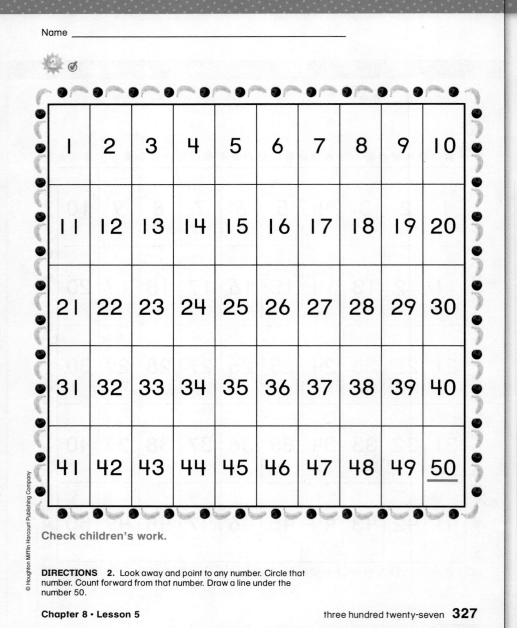

Name _____

1	2	3	4	5	6	7	8	9	10
11	12	13	14	15	16	17	18	19	20
21	22	23	24	25	26	27	28	29	30
31	32	33	34	35	36	37	38	39	40
41	42	43	44	45	46	47	48	49	50

© Houghton Mifflin Harcourt Publishing Company

Check children's work.

DIRECTIONS   2. Look away and point to any number. Circle that number. Count forward from that number. Draw a line under the number 50.

Chapter 8 • Lesson 5   three hundred twenty-seven **327**

Cross-Curricular   SCIENCE

Materials self-stick notes, chart paper

• Draw a fifty chart on chart paper, leaving each square large enough to hold a self-stick note. Next to it, write: **day, night, day, night, day, night.** Establish that day follows night and night follows day. Refer to it as a sequence, or order, that never changes.

• Recall that numbers have sequence, or order, too.

• Write the following on self-stick notes and show them on the board in this order: 44, 35, 40, 43, 38, 36, 41, 42, 39, 37. Have children place one self-stick note at a time on the fifty chart until the numbers are in order.

day	night	day	night	day	night

SOCIAL STUDIES

Materials chart paper

• Discuss the difference between needs and wants. Explain that food is a need and that a toy is a want.

• Talk about basic needs that people have such as shelter and food.

• Make a chart with the following information:

30 apples	27 apples	25 apples
26 apples	28 apples	29 apples

• Read the chart with children. Have children put the numbers on the chart in order and count from the greatest number to 50.

PROBLEM SOLVING

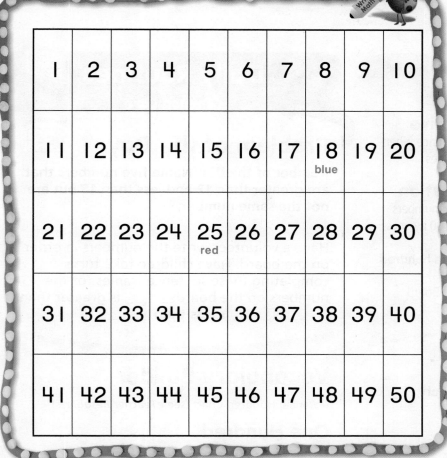

1	2	3	4	5	6	7	8	9	10
11	12	13	14	15	16	17	18 blue	19	20
21	22	23	24	25 red	26	27	28	29	30
31	32	33	34	35	36	37	38	39	40
41	42	43	44	45	46	47	48	49	50

DIRECTIONS I am greater than 17 and less than 19. What number am I? Use blue to color that number. I am greater than 24 and less than 26. What number am I? Use red to color that number.

HOME ACTIVITY • Think of a number between 1 and 50. Say *greater than* and *less than* to describe your number. Have your child say the number.

328 three hundred twenty-eight

© Houghton Mifflin Harcourt Publishing Company

FOR MORE PRACTICE:
Standards Practice Book, pp. P159–P160

▶ **Problem Solving** (MATHEMATICAL PRACTICES)

Explain to children that they are going to use the fifty chart to solve riddles.

Read the first riddle aloud.

- **What number is greater than 17 and less than 19?** 18 **Color the number blue.**
- **How did you know which number to color blue?** Possible answer: I found 17 on the fifty chart. I used the counting order to see that 18 is one greater than 17 and one less than 19.

Read the next riddle aloud.

- **What number is greater than 24 and less than 26?** 25 **Use red to color the number.**

4 SUMMARIZE (MATHEMATICAL PRACTICES)

Essential Question

How does the order of numbers help you count to 50 by ones? When I know the counting order, I know what number to say after each number. If I start with 1 and say each number in counting order, I can count from 1 to 50.

Differentiated Instruction   INDEPENDENT ACTIVITIES

Grab-and-Go!
Differentiated Centers Kit

Activities
Place Your Order

Children complete the purple Activity Card 20 by identifying the numbers 10 through 20.

Literature
Counting at the Market

Children read the book and count fruit and vegetables up to 30.

Games
Sweet and Sour Path

Children increase familiarity with numbers from 1 to 30 with repeated counting forward to move along the game path.

Digital Path

- Animated Math Models
- iT iTools
- MM HMH Mega Math
- Soar to Success Math
- GO MATH! eStudent Edition

Count to 100 by Ones

LESSON AT A GLANCE

Common Core Standard
Know number names and the count sequence.
CC.K.CC.1 Count to 100 by ones and by tens.
Also CC.K.CC.2

Lesson Objective
Know the count sequence when counting to 100 by ones.

Essential Question
How does the order of numbers help you to count to 100 by ones?

Vocabulary one hundred

Materials MathBoard

Digital Path

 Animated Math Models

iT iTools: Number Chart

eStudent Edition

COMMON CORE
PROFESSIONAL
DEVELOPMENT

About the Math

Teaching for Depth

John Van de Walle recommended in his book, *Elementary and Middle School Mathematics, Teaching Developmentally*, that teachers encourage children to explore counting patterns on hundred charts.

In this lesson, children are first introduced to the hundred chart. They will begin to identify patterns in the sequence of numbers. They will look for relationships between "neighboring numbers."

Even though children in Kindergarten may not have an understanding of place value, they can learn much about the sequence of numbers to 100 by using the hundred chart.

Professional Development Video Podcasts

Daily Routines

Math Board

Common Core

SPIRAL REVIEW

Problem of the Day

eTransparency
8.6

Number of the Day Name five numbers that are greater than 12 and less than 18 but are not the same number.

13, 14, 15, 16, 17

Have a volunteer write the numbers in order on the board. Have children take turns completing these sentence frames for the numbers on the board: _____ **is greater than** _____; _____ **is less than** _____.

Vocabulary Builder

Materials Hundred Chart (see *eTeacher Resources*)

One Hundred

Show children a hundred chart.

- **Each square represents one. How many ones are in the first row?** 10

- **Each row represents a set of 10 ones.**

Count with children the number of rows in the chart, circling each row after you have counted it.

- **How many sets are there in all?** 10

- **One hundred is 10 sets of 10 ones.**

1	2	3	4	5	6	7	8	9	10
11	12	13	14	15	16	17	18	19	20
21	22	23	24	25	26	27	28	29	30
31	32	33	34	35	36	37	38	39	40
41	42	43	44	45	46	47	48	49	50
51	52	53	54	55	56	57	58	59	60
61	62	63	64	65	66	67	68	69	70
71	72	73	74	75	76	77	78	79	80
81	82	83	84	85	86	87	88	89	90
91	92	93	94	95	96	97	98	99	100

Differentiated Instruction Activities

ⓔⓛⓛ Language Support
🕐 Auditory / Visual
Small Group

Strategy: Model Concepts

Materials Hundred Chart (see *eTeacher Resources*)

Children can count to 100 using counting patterns if they are illustrated.

- Have children point to each number on the hundred chart as they count to 100.

- To help children identify the counting pattern, have them emphasize the digits that repeat each decade as they point to them on the hundred chart: **twenty-ONE, twenty-TWO, twenty-THREE...**

See ⓔⓛⓛ Activity Guide for leveled activities.

Enrich
🕐 Mathematical / Visual
Individual / Small Group

Materials 10 × 10 Grid (see *eTeacher Resources*)

Distribute grids and let children color squares to create simple pictures or designs.

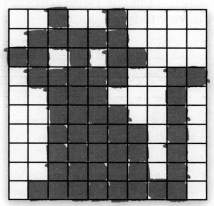

- Have children count the number of colored squares and write the number. Then have them count forward from that number to 100. Display children's work.

▲ RtI Response to Intervention

Reteach Tier 1
🕐 Interpersonal / Social
Whole Class

Materials large ball

Have children stand or sit in a big circle. Give the ball to a volunteer. Have the volunteer demonstrate how to carefully give the ball to the child on his or her left.

- Explain to children that they will be passing the ball around the circle as they count from 1 to 100. **Say the next number each time the ball is passed.** Lead children as they pass the ball and count aloud together to 100.

Repeat the activity. Instead of counting together as a class, have the child who receives the ball say the next number.

Tier 2
🕐 Visual
Small Group

Materials Hundred Chart, Spinners (7- and 8-section) (see *eTeacher Resources*)

Label the spinner with numbers 39, 44, 57, 65, 79, 82, 93, and 100. Let a child spin a number and circle the number on a hundred chart. Repeat.

- Point to the first circled number and ask a child to name it. Have children count from this number to the other circled number. Have a volunteer point to the numbers on the hundred chart as the group counts aloud.

Repeat the activity with different numbers.

1 ENGAGE

Materials Calendar (see *eTeacher Resources*)

Access Prior Knowledge Explain to the children that they are going to fill in the name and numbers on the calendar for the current month.

Write the number 1 on the first day of the calendar.

- **What number will come next?** 2

Have a volunteer write the number.

Remind children where to write the next number after completing a row. Continue until you have had children fill in the dates through the month. Then have children count the numbers in order.

2 TEACH and TALK   GO Online   Animated Math Models

► **Listen and Draw**   MATHEMATICAL PRACTICES

Read the problem aloud as children listen.

Brandon wants to read the numbers on a hundred chart. What will be the first number he says? What will be the last number he says?

- **Look at this chart of numbers. It is called a hundred chart.**

Explain that it is similar to a fifty chart because it has rows and has numbers in order. It is a hundred chart because it has the numbers 1 to 100.

- **What is the first number on the hundred chart?** 1
- **What will be the first number Brandon says?** 1
- **How can you use the top row of the chart to count?** Point to each number across the row and say them in order.
- **When you reach the end of the top row, how can you continue your counting?** Go down to the beginning of the next row.

Have children point to each number as they count to 100 on the chart. Check to be sure they move correctly from row to row. Stop at the end of each row after children reach 20. Discuss the new tens number and remind them that this number is used to name the numbers in the next row.

- **What is the last number on the hundred chart?** 100
- **What will be the last number Brandon says?** 100

MATHEMATICAL PRACTICES **Why should everyone count the same way?**

COMMON CORE
CC.K.CC.1 Count to 100 by ones and by tens.

Name _____

Count to 100 by Ones

Essential Question How does the order of numbers help you count to 100 by ones?

COMMON CORE STANDARD CC.K.CC.1
Know number names and the count sequence.

Lesson 8.6

Listen and Draw

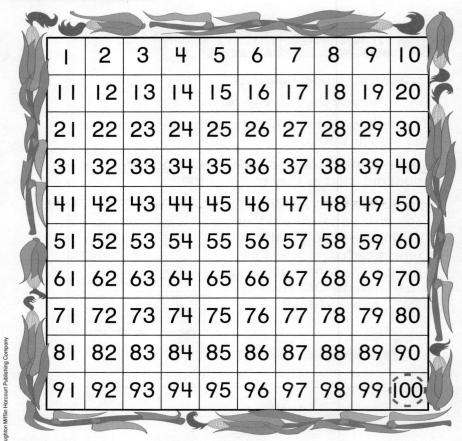

1	2	3	4	5	6	7	8	9	10
11	12	13	14	15	16	17	18	19	20
21	22	23	24	25	26	27	28	29	30
31	32	33	34	35	36	37	38	39	40
41	42	43	44	45	46	47	48	49	50
51	52	53	54	55	56	57	58	59	60
61	62	63	64	65	66	67	68	69	70
71	72	73	74	75	76	77	78	79	80
81	82	83	84	85	86	87	88	89	90
91	92	93	94	95	96	97	98	99	100

DIRECTIONS Point to each number as you count to 100. Trace the circle around the number 100.

Check children's work.

Chapter 8 · Lesson 6

three hundred twenty-nine **329**

Standards Practice 8.6   Common Core   SPIRAL REVIEW

Name _____

Count to 100 by Ones

COMMON CORE STANDARD CC.K.CC.1
Know number names and the count sequence.

Lesson 8.6

❶

1	2	3	4	5	6	7	8	9	10
11	12	13	14	15	16	17	18	19	20
21	22	23	24	25	26	27	28	29	30
31	32	33	34	35	36	37	38	39	40
41	42	43	44	45	46	47	48	49	50
51	52	53	54	55	56	57	58	59	60
61	62	63	64	65	66	67	68	69	70
71	72	73	74	75	76	77	78	79	80
81	82	83	84	85	86	87	88	89	90
91	92	93	94	95	96	97	98	99	100

Check children's work.

DIRECTIONS 1. Point to each number as you count to 100. Look away and point to any number. Circle that number. Count forward to 100 from that number. Draw a line under the number 100.

Chapter 8

one hundred sixty-one **P161**

Lesson Check (CC.K.CC.1)   ★TEST PREP

❶

71	72	73	74	75	76	77	78	79	80
81	82	83	84	85	86	87	88	89	90
91	92	93	94	95	96	97	98	99	100

80 ○   81 ●   82 ○   90 ○

Spiral Review (CC.K.CC.6, CC.K.OA.5)

□ □ □ □

$3 - 1 = 2$	$3 - 2 = 1$	$4 - 2 = 2$	$4 - 3 = 1$
○	○	○	●

❸

DIRECTIONS 1. Begin with 71 and count forward to 80. What is the next number? Mark under your answer. (Lesson 8.6) 2. Pete makes the cube train shown. He takes the cube train apart to show how many cubes are gray. Mark under the subtraction sentence that shows Pete's cube train. (Lesson 6.4) 3. Which set shows the number of roses is the same as the number of daisies? (Lesson 2.1)

P162 one hundred sixty-two

Share and Show

1	2	3	4	5	6	7	8	9	10
(11)	12	13	14	15	16	17	18	19	20
21	22	23	24	25	26	27	28	29	30
31	32	33	34	35	36	37	38	39	40
41	42	43	44	45	46	47	48	49	50
51	52	53	54	55	56	57	58	59	60
61	62	63	64	65	66	67	68	69	70
71	72	73	74	75	76	77	78	79	80
81	82	83	84	85	86	87	88	89	90
91	92	93	94	95	96	97	98	99	__100__

© Houghton Mifflin Harcourt Publishing Company

DIRECTIONS 1. Point to each number as you count to 100. Circle the number 11. Begin with 11 and count forward to 100. Draw a line under the number 100.

330 three hundred thirty

---

3 PRACTICE

▶ **Share and Show** • **Guided Practice**

- **What do you see on this page?** a hundred chart
- **How do you know that it is a hundred chart?** It has the numbers 1 to 100 in order.

Show children a hundred chart.

- **Point to each number on the chart as you count aloud to 100.**
- **Find the number 11. Circle it.**
- **Begin at 11 and count forward to 20.**
- **What is the same about all the numbers you counted except 20?** They start with 1.
- **How did the numbers change as you counted from 11 to 19?** They ended with the numbers 1 to 9 in order.
- **Draw a line below the number 10.**
- **Now begin at 11 and count forward to 100.**

Have children repeat this activity by counting forward from 61 to 70 and from 91 to 100.

- **Point to each number as we count. 1, 2, 3 ... 98, 99, 100.**

Remind children how to move to the next row when they reach the end of each row.

Reteach 8.6

Name _____

Lesson 8.6
Reteach

Count to 100 by Ones

COMMON CORE STANDARD CC.K.CC.1
Know number names and the
count sequence.

1 Check children's work.

1	2	3	4	5	6	7	8	9	10
11	12	13	14	15	16	17	18	19	20
21	22	23	24	25	26	27	28	29	30
31	32	33	34	35	36	37	38	39	40
41	42	43	44	45	46	47	48	49	50
51	52	53	54	55	56	57	58	59	60
61	62	63	64	65	66	67	68	69	70
71	72	73	74	75	76	77	78	79	80
81	82	83	84	85	86	87	88	89	90
91	92	93	94	95	96	97	98	99	100

DIRECTIONS 1. Count forward from 1. Draw a dot on each number as you count. Begin with 97 and count forward to 100. Color those numbers yellow.

Reteach
© Houghton Mifflin Harcourt Publishing Company

R66

Grade K

Enrich 8.6

Name _____

Lesson 8.6
Enrich

Complete the Hundred Chart

COMMON CORE STANDARD CC.K.CC.1
Know number names and the
count sequence.

1

1	2	3	4	5	6	7	8	9	10
11	12	13	14	15	16	17	18	19	20
21	22	23	24	25	26	27	28	29	30
31	32	33	34	35	36	37	38	39	40
41	42	43	44	45	46	47	48	49	50
51	52	53	54	55	56	57	58	59	60
61	62	63	64	65	66	67	68	69	70
71	72	73	74	75	76	(77)	78	79	80
81	82	83	84	85	86	87	88	89	90
91	92	93	94	95	96	97	98	99	100

Check children's work.

DIRECTIONS 1. Point to each number as you count to 100. Tell the missing numbers. Find the number that is greater than 76 and less than 78. Circle the number. Find the number that is greater than 98 and less than 100. Draw a line under the number.

Enrich
© Houghton Mifflin Harcourt Publishing Company

E66

Grade K

⚠ COMMON ERRORS

Error Children may not count all of the numbers as they use the chart to count.

Example Children count 61, 62, 64, 65, 66, 68, 70.

Springboard to Learning Instead of picking up their fingers after they say a number and then pointing to the next number, have children slide their fingers across each row, stopping on each successive number.

Lesson 8.6 330

► More Practice

Explain to children that they will count the numbers on this hundred chart as they did on the last page. Then suggest that children place one hand on the hundred chart. They will look away, lift the hand slightly, and then point to a number. They circle the number, count forward from this number to 100, and draw a line under 100.

Use Exercise 2 for **Quick Check**.

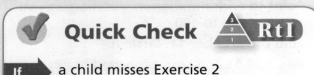

Quick Check

If → a child misses Exercise 2

Then → **Differentiate Instruction** with
- RtI Tier 1 Activity, p. 329B
- Reteach 8.6
- Soar to Success Math 28.11

H.O.T. Problem Darlene counts forward from 1 and stops at 87. The teacher asks Julio to continue counting to 100. What numbers does Julio say? 88, 89, 90, 91, 92, 93, 94, 95, 96, 97, 98, 99, 100.

Go Deeper
MATHEMATICAL PRACTICES

Children should be able to use what they know about counting to 100 to continue a counting pattern, starting from a given number. They should be able to explain how they know what numbers follow 87 to end at 100.

1	2	3	4	5	6	7	8	9	10
11	12	13	14	15	16	17	18	19	20
21	22	23	24	25	26	27	28	29	30
31	32	33	34	35	36	37	38	39	40
41	42	43	44	45	46	47	48	49	50
51	52	53	54	55	56	57	58	59	60
61	62	63	64	65	66	67	68	69	70
71	72	73	74	75	76	77	78	79	80
81	82	83	84	85	86	87	88	89	90
91	92	93	94	95	96	97	98	99	100

© Houghton Mifflin Harcourt Publishing Company

DIRECTIONS 2. Point to each number as you count to 100. Look away and point to any number. Circle that number. Count forward to 100 from that number. Draw a line under the number 100.

Check children's work.

Chapter 8 • Lesson 6

three hundred thirty-one **331**

COMMON CORE
PROFESSIONAL DEVELOPMENT

Math Talk in Action

Teacher:	How did you find your number to start in Exercise 2?
Dan:	I looked away and put my finger on 24.
Mai:	I pointed to 81.
Pete:	I pointed to 63.
Teacher:	How did you count from your number to 100?
Dan:	I said each number on the row after my number; but then I forgot where to look next on the chart. The last number I counted was 30.
Teacher:	Who knows what Dan should do when he gets to 30?

Pete:	You have to move your finger from the 30 to the beginning of the next line and say all the numbers in that row. You do that for every row until you get to 100.
Mai:	Your number was at the top of the chart, Dan, so you had to count the numbers on a lot of rows. My number was 81 and it was at the bottom of the chart. I did not have so many numbers to count.
Dan:	I am going to count from my number to 100. I know how to do that now. Thanks, Pete and Mai.
Teacher:	Great teamwork class! It helps when you work together to solve problems.

PROBLEM SOLVING

❶

1	2	3	4	5	6	7	8	9	10
11	12	13	14	15	16	17	18	19	20
21	22	23	24	25	26	27	28	29	30

❷

Check children's work.

DIRECTIONS 1. Place your finger on the number 15. Write to show the numbers that are "neighbors" to the number 15. Say *greater than* and *less than* to describe the numbers. 2. Draw to show what you know about some other "neighbor" numbers in the chart.

HOME ACTIVITY • Show your child a calendar. Point to a number on the calendar. Have him or her tell you all the numbers that are "neighbors" to that number.

332 three hundred thirty-two

FOR MORE PRACTICE:
Standards Practice Book, pp. P161–P162

▶ **Problem Solving**

Have children point to 15 in Exercise 1.

- **The numbers around 15 are called the neighbors of 15.**

- **What number would be just before 15?** 14 **Write it. Use the term *less than* to describe the numbers.** 14 is less than 15.

- **What number is just after 15?** 16 **Write it. Use the term *greater than* to describe these numbers.** 16 is greater than 15.

- **How can you find the number that is just above 15 on the chart?** I know that 5 is one greater than 4 and one less than 6. I know that 5 is 10 less than 15. **Write it.**

- **How can you find the number that is just below 15 on the chart?** I know that 25 is one greater than 24 and one less than 26. I know that 25 is 10 more than 15. **Write it.**

Discuss ideas about other neighbor numbers in the chart. Have children share their drawings with a friend.

❹ SUMMARIZE

Essential Question

How does the order of numbers help you count to 100 by ones? When I know the order of numbers, I can start counting from any number and count by ones to 100.

Differentiated Instruction — INDEPENDENT ACTIVITIES

Grab-and-Go!™
Differentiated Centers Kit

Activities
Place Your Order

Children complete the purple Activity Card 20 by identifying the numbers 10 through 20.

Literature
Counting at the Market

Children read the book and count fruit and vegetables up to 30.

Games
Sweet and Sour Path

Children increase familiarity with numbers from 1 to 30 with repeated counting forward to move along the game path.

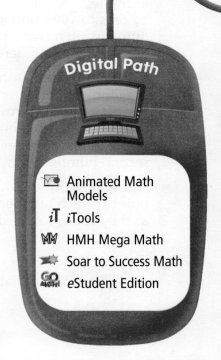

Digital Path

- Animated Math Models
- *iT* iTools
- HMH Mega Math
- Soar to Success Math
- *e*Student Edition

Count to 100 by Tens

LESSON AT A GLANCE

Common Core Standard
Know number names and the count sequence.
CC.K.CC.1 Count to 100 by ones and by tens.

Lesson Objective
Know the count sequence when counting to 100 by tens.

Essential Question
How can you count to 100 by tens on a hundred chart?

Vocabulary **tens**

Materials MathBoard

Digital Path

 Animated Math Models

iT *i*Tools: Number Chart

eStudent Edition

About the Math

COMMON CORE PROFESSIONAL DEVELOPMENT

Why Teach This

In this lesson, children have multiple opportunities to count by tens to 100 using a hundred chart. They fill in missing numbers on a chart and continue to discuss relationships between the numbers and their neighbors on the chart.

As children work with a hundred chart, it is important that they look for patterns in the way that numbers are made. For example, each row of ten has a pattern using the 1 to 9 order. Also, each number in the last column has a pattern with the first number being in the 1 to 9 order and the second number always a 0.

As children use the hundred chart, suggest they touch or point to each number as they count. This will help them as they count forward starting with different numbers than 1 or 10.

 Professional Development Video Podcasts

Daily Routines
Common Core

Math Board

SPIRAL REVIEW

Problem of the Day

eTransparency **8.7**

Number of the Day I am thinking of a number that is two less than 30. What is it? I am thinking of a number that has two zeros. You can find it on a hundred chart. What is that number?
28; 100

Continue asking riddles about numbers to 100 for children to solve.

Fluency Builder

Counting Tape

Materials Counting Tape

 EVERY DAY COUNTS®

If you have not yet had a Day 100 discussion, be sure to do that when the day arrives, and continue to use the same sequence of colors for Day 101 and beyond.

Use the color pattern to draw students' attention to the similarities between the first numbers on the Tape and those just after 100. If they discover the predictability of the counting sequence, they may develop confidence in counting larger quantities.

- **What number will you write today?**
- **Let's look at the last numbers you have on the Tape. Does anyone see a similar group of numbers somewhere else on the Tape?**
- **What do you notice is the same about every red square?** The numbers all end with the same number.

Differentiated Instruction Activities

ELL Language Support
🕐 Visual / Small Group

Strategy: Describe

Materials Hundred Chart (see *eTeacher Resources*), crayons

Children can demonstrate their understanding of number patterns by describing them.

• Have a volunteer color the first column of a hundred chart. **Describe how the numbers end.** They end with 1. **Describe how the numbers begin.** Possible answer: It is like counting from 1 to 9.

• Continue by having other volunteers color the last column on the chart. Have children describe the numbers in the column.

Repeat the activity with a new hundred chart. Have children color and describe rows instead of columns.

See **ELL** Activity Guide for leveled activities.

Enrich
🕐 Logical / Mathematical Small Group

Materials Hundred Chart (see *eTeacher Resources*)

Suggest that children listen to clues in order to find a "secret number" on a hundred chart.

• **My secret number is between 60 and 80. It comes right after 69. What is my secret number?** 70 Have a child circle 70 on a hundred chart.

• **When you were listening to my riddle, how did you know where to look on the hundred chart?** Possible answer: I know the numbers between 60 and 80 are near the bottom of the chart and 69 is near the last column, so I looked at the end of that row.

Repeat with other numbers.

▲ RtI Response to Intervention

Reteach Tier 1
🕐 Logical / Mathematical Whole Class / Small Group

Materials Hundred Chart (see *eTeacher Resources*), two-color counters

Have children look at a hundred chart. Point to the column that begins with 10. **How are these numbers alike?** They all end with 0.

• Give children a hundred chart and a counter. Explain that one child should cover a number in the tens column. Another child should count forward from that number by tens to 100.

Have children take turns, repeating the activity several times so they practice counting to 100 by tens.

Tier 2
🕐 Logical / Mathematical Small Group

Materials Hundred Chart (see *eTeacher Resources*), connecting cubes

Have children count by tens in order on a hundred chart. **Where are the numbers that end with 0?** in the last column **How many numbers are in a row?** 10

• Put a cube on 10. Have children count with you as you count by tens. **What number do we count next?** 20 Put a cube on 20.

• **If we count by tens, where will the next cube go?** on 30 Have children count aloud to check the prediction. Put a cube on 30.

Continue similarly. Each time, have children tell where the next cube will go before you count.

1 ENGAGE

Materials Hundred Chart (see *eTeacher Resources*)

Access Prior Knowledge Explain to children that they are going to read a hundred chart together.

- **What number do you read first when you read the hundred chart?** 1

Have children read aloud the numbers across the first row of the hundred chart.

- **What number will we read next?** 11

Have children read together the rest of the chart as they point to the numbers.

2 TEACH and TALK 🔵 GO Online Animated Math Models

▶ **Listen and Draw** (MATHEMATICAL PRACTICES)

Read the problem aloud as children listen.

Olivia is using a hundred chart to count to 100. She wants to find a faster way to get to 100 than counting by ones. What is another way that Olivia can count to 100?

- **Look at the hundred chart. Circle all the numbers that end in zero.**
- **Look at the numbers you circled. What can you tell about these numbers?** All the numbers end in zero. The first part of the numbers goes up by 1 each time.
- **What is the first number you circled?** 10
- **Start with 10 and say the numbers you circled in order.** 10, 20, 30, ..., 100

Explain to children that each number circled is 10 more than the circled number before. Have children count several rows to check. Point out that, for this reason, the numbers they circled are called tens.

- **Tell a friend how you are counting.** by tens

Reread the word problem.

- **What is a faster way for Olivia to use the hundred chart to count to 100?** by tens

---

COMMON CORE

CC.K.CC.1 Count to 100 by ones and by tens.

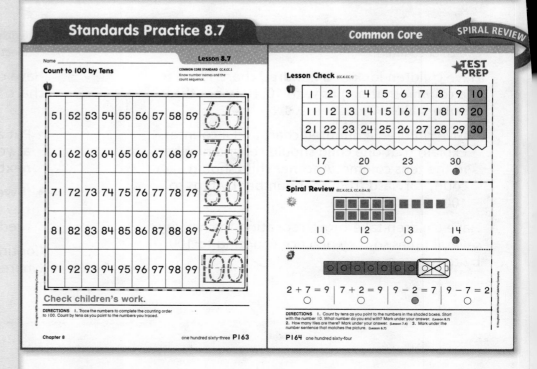

Share and Show

1	2	3	4	5	6	7	8	9	10
11	12	13	14	15	16	17	18	19	20
21	22	23	24	25	26	27	28	29	30
31	32	33	34	35	36	37	38	39	40
41	42	43	44	45	46	47	48	49	50

Check children's work.

DIRECTIONS 1. Write the numbers to complete the counting order to 20. Trace the numbers to complete the counting order to 50. Count by tens as you point to the numbers you wrote and traced.

334 three hundred thirty-four

▶ Share and Show • Guided Practice

- **What do you see on this page?** a fifty chart with some missing numbers
- **Start with 1. Point to each number and count until you get to the place where a number is missing.** 1, 2, 3, ..., 9
- **What is the missing number?** 10 **How do you know?** Possible answers: 10 is the next number after 9 when you count; 10 is 1 greater than 9. **Write 10.**

Have children repeat for the remaining rows, writing or tracing 20, 30, 40, and 50.

- **Look at the numbers you wrote. What is the special name for these numbers?** tens
- **Start with 10. Count by tens as you point to the numbers you wrote and traced.** 10, 20, 30, 40, 50
- **How did you just count to 50?** by tens

Reteach 8.7

RtI

Name _____

Lesson 8.7
Reteach

Count to 100 by Tens

COMMON CORE STANDARD CC.K.CC.1
Know number names and the count sequence.

1	2	3	4	5	6	7	8	9	10
11	12	13	14	15	16	17	18	19	20
21	22	23	24	25	26	27	28	29	30
31	32	33	34	35	36	37	38	39	40
41	42	43	44	45	46	47	48	49	50
51	52	53	54	55	56	57	58	59	60
61	62	63	64	65	66	67	68	69	70
71	72	73	74	75	76	77	78	79	80
81	82	83	84	85	86	87	88	89	90
91	92	93	94	95	96	97	98	99	100

Check children's work.

DIRECTIONS 1. Color the boxes of all the numbers that end with a zero. Count by tens as you point to the numbers in the boxes you colored.

Reteach
© Houghton Mifflin Harcourt Publishing Company

R67

Grade K

Enrich 8.7

Name _____

Lesson 8.7
Enrich

Color a Ten

COMMON CORE STANDARD CC.K.CC.1
Know number names and the count sequence.

1	2	3	4	5	6	7	8	9	10
11	12	13	14	15	16	17	18	19	20
21	22	23	24	25	26	27	28	29	30
31	32	33	34	35	36	37	38	39	40
41	42	43	44	45	46	47	48	49	50
51	52	53	54	55	56	57	58	59	60
61	62	63	64	65	66	67	68	69	70
71	72	73	74	75	76	77	78	79	80
81	82	83	84	85	86	87	88	89	90
91	92	93	94	95	96	97	98	99	100

Children should color the box for 40 yellow, 70 red, and 90 orange.

DIRECTIONS 1. Count by tens as you point to the numbers. Then find the ten that is greater than 30 and less than 50. Color that number yellow. Find the ten that is greater than 80 and less than 100. Color that number orange. Find the ten that is greater than 60 and less than 80. Color that number red.

Enrich
© Houghton Mifflin Harcourt Publishing Company

E67

Grade K

⚠ COMMON ERRORS

Error Children may count incorrectly when counting by tens.

Example Children count 30 after 10.

Springboard to Learning Show children the last column of a hundred chart. Point out that the first part of each number goes up by one each time.

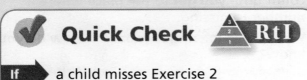

▶ **More Practice**

Have children locate Exercise 2.

- **Count forward from 51 to 100. Trace each missing number when you come to it.**

Have children point to the numbers they have traced and count together by tens.

Use Exercise 2 for **Quick Check**.

 Quick Check ▲ RtI

If ➡ a child misses Exercise 2

Then ➡ **Differentiate Instruction** with
- RtI Tier 1 Activity, p. 333B
- Reteach 8.7
- ⭐ Soar to Success Math 28.25

H.O.T. Problem Can you tell without looking at a hundred chart which number is below 34? **Explain.** Yes; possible answer: I know that the first part of the number goes up by 1 and the other number stays the same. The number is 44.

Go Deeper

Children should be able to use what they know about a hundred chart to solve this problem. Ask about different numbers and discuss patterns children see in the hundred chart.

Name _____

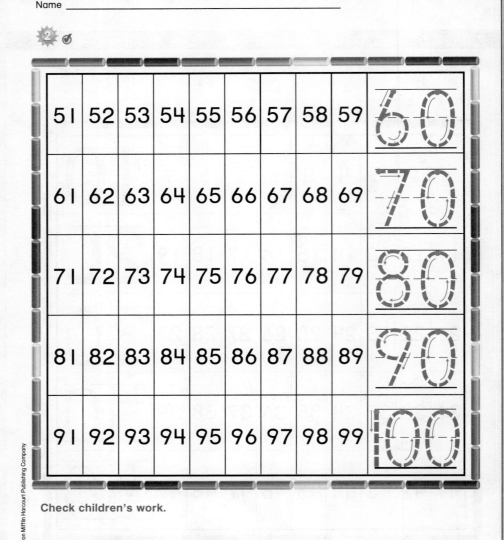

Check children's work.

DIRECTIONS 2. Trace the numbers to complete the counting order to 100. Count by tens as you point to the numbers you traced.

Chapter 8 · Lesson 7 three hundred thirty-five **335**

© Houghton Mifflin Harcourt Publishing Company

COMMON CORE
PROFESSIONAL DEVELOPMENT

Mathematical Practices in Your Classroom

CC.K–12.MP.4 Model with Mathematics.

Understanding relationships between numbers helps children make sense of the world in a mathematical way.

- Children who are confident in their counting abilities are more comfortable attempting to solve problems in everyday life. Children who have a firm sense of the order of numbers are better able to solve everyday problems such as counting money or following steps in a recipe.
- Children use their counting abilities to solve more complex problems, such as by writing an addition or subtraction equation to describe a situation.
- In this lesson, children count to 100 by tens using a hundred chart. The hundred chart helps them build relationships between numbers.

They can begin to see patterns in numbering, such as counting by fives and tens.

Provide opportunities for children to describe how they use the hundred chart to learn about numbers.

- **How is counting from 91 to 100 like counting from 11 to 20 on a number chart?** You read the numbers across the row. Each number is one more than the last one. 11 and 91 end in 1, 12 and 92 end in 2, and so on across the rows.
- **How does using a hundred chart help you learn the counting sequence?** I can see all the numbers in order. I can see ways the numbers are alike and different.

PROBLEM SOLVING

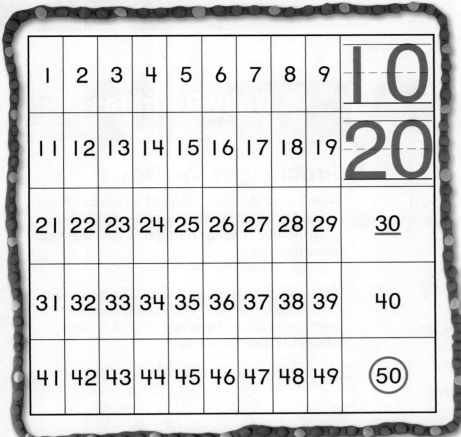

1	2	3	4	5	6	7	8	9	10
11	12	13	14	15	16	17	18	19	20
21	22	23	24	25	26	27	28	29	30
31	32	33	34	35	36	37	38	39	40
41	42	43	44	45	46	47	48	49	50

DIRECTIONS Tony has 10 marbles. Write the number in order. Jenny has ten more marbles than Tony. Write that number in order. Lindsay has ten more marbles than Jenny. Draw a line under the number that shows how many marbles Lindsay has. When counting by tens, what number comes right after 40? Circle the number.

HOME ACTIVITY · Show your child a calendar. Use self-stick notes to cover random numbers. Ask your child to say the numbers that are covered. Then have him or her remove the self-stick note to check.

336 three hundred thirty-six

© Houghton Mifflin Harcourt Publishing Company

FOR MORE PRACTICE:
Standards Practice Book, pp. P163–P164

▶ **Problem Solving** **MATHEMATICAL PRACTICES**

Ask children what they notice about the fifty chart. Some numbers are missing.

- **Tony has 10 marbles. Where will you write 10 on the chart?** at the end of the first row

- **Jenny has ten more than Tony. How many does she have?** 20 **Write the number in order on the chart.**

- **Lindsay has ten more marbles than Jenny. How many does Lindsay have?** 30 **Draw a line under the number to show how many marbles Lindsay has.**

- **What number comes right after 40 when you are counting by tens?** 50 **Circle that number.**

 Children may wish to place this page in their Math Journals.

4 SUMMARIZE **MATHEMATICAL PRACTICES**

Essential Question

How can you count to 100 by tens on a hundred chart? I can find 10 on the hundred chart. Then I can look down that column and say each number to count by tens.

Count by Tens

LESSON AT A GLANCE

Common Core Standard
Know number names and the count sequence.
CC.K.CC.1 Count to 100 by ones and by tens.

Lesson Objective
Use sets of tens to count to 100.

Essential Question
How can you use sets of tens to count to 100?

Materials MathBoard

Digital Path

 Animated Math Models

iT iTools: Number Chart

GO eStudent Edition

COMMON CORE PROFESSIONAL DEVELOPMENT

About the Math

Teaching for Depth

In this lesson, children use sets of ten objects to practice counting by tens. Counting sets of tens is a means of describing quantities. For example, two sets of ten is a way of describing 20 objects.

Sets of ten should be accepted as standing for a single set which can then be counted (10, 20, 30). Counting by sets is a new idea for children who have never thought about counting a set of ten objects as a single set.

As children count sets of objects, ask them questions to help them construct knowledge about the relationship between the sets of tens and individual objects, such as:

- **How can we really be sure that this set shows 30 cubes?**

- **What number do you think we will get if we count these cubes one by one?**

 Professional Development Video Podcasts

Daily Routines
Common Core

SPIRAL REVIEW

Math Board

Problem of the Day
eTransparency **8.8**

Number of the Day Think of a number from 10 to 20. What number is two greater than your number? What number is two less than your number?

Answers depend on number chosen.

After children have answered the questions about their number, have them choose another number between 20 and 30 and answer the same questions.

Vocabulary Builder

Materials connecting cubes

Tens

Count each connecting cube from 1 to 20 with children.

- **How many connecting cubes are there in all?** 20

Make two ten-cube trains with the connecting cubes.

- **Tens are a set of 10 ones. How many sets of 10 ones do you have?** 2

Repeat this activity with 30, 40, and 50 connecting cubes.

Differentiated Instruction Activities

ELL Language Support
 Kinesthetic | Small Group

Strategy: Model Concepts

Materials connecting cubes

Children understand a concept when it is modeled.

- Give each group 50 connecting cubes.
- Explain that putting the cubes in groups of tens makes it easier to count larger numbers.
- Children use 20 cubes to make sets of 10.
- Children count the tens and write the number.
- The activity is repeated using 30, 40, and 50 cubes.

See **ELL** Activity Guide for leveled activities.

Enrich
 Kinesthetic | Small Group

Materials Numeral Cards (0–7), (8–15) (see *eTeacher Resources*), connecting cubes

Children place numeral cards 1 to 10 facedown. Provide small groups with 100 cubes.

- Have one child pick a card, another child model that number of tens with cubes, and another child write how many tens.
- Have children switch roles and repeat the activity until all of the cards have been taken.

RtI Response to Intervention

Reteach Tier 1
 Kinesthetic / Visual | Whole Class / Small Group

Materials Ten Frames (see *eTeacher Resources*), connecting cubes

Provide each group with 100 cubes. Have one child in the group place a cube in each box of a ten-frame. When they have one set of 10, they connect the cubes, making a ten-cube train.

- Children take turns placing cubes in the frame and making trains until all the cubes have been used.
- **How many cubes are in each train?** 10
- **How many sets of 10 are there?** 10
- **How many cubes in all?** 100
- Have children point to each train as they count by tens.

Tier 2
 Visual / Kinesthetic | Small Group

Materials connecting cubes, Spinners (5- and 6-section) (see *eTeacher Resources*)

Provide each group with 100 cubes and a 5-section spinner labeled with numbers from 1 to 5.

- Have children take turns spinning and taking the number of cubes shown on the spinner. Have them put them together to make a cube train.
- Then have each child add more cubes to make a ten-cube train. Have them count the cube trains by tens to find the number in all.

1 ENGAGE

Materials Hundred Chart (see *eTeacher Resources*)

Access Prior Knowledge Show a hundred chart on the board.

- **What numbers end with 0?** 10, 20, 30, 40, 50, 60, 70, 80, 90, 100
- **Where are these numbers found on the hundred chart?** in the last column
- **If we count from 10 by tens, what will be the next number we count?** 20

Have children count with you as you count forward by tens to 100.

2 TEACH and TALK

GO Online | Animated Math Models

▶ **Listen and Draw** (MATHEMATICAL PRACTICES)

Read the problem aloud as children listen.

Caden wants to make models to show counting by tens. How can he use cube towers to show counting by tens to 50?

Remind children how they counted by tens using the hundred chart. Make sure they realize that there are 10 cubes in each cube tower. Have children point to each set of cube towers as they count by tens.

- **What does one cube tower show?** 10 **Trace the number.**
- **How many do two sets of cube towers show?** 20 **Trace the number.**
- **How many do three sets of cube towers show?** 30 **Trace the number.**

Continue asking similar questions as children point to the cube tower models for 40 and 50, tracing the number for each.

- **Count the cube towers by tens.** 10, 20, 30, 40, 50

Read the word problem again.

- **How can Caden use cube towers to show counting by tens to 50?** Possible answer: He can build five ten-cube towers. Then he can count by tens. 10, 20, 30, 40, 50

COMMON CORE | **CC.K.CC.1** Count to 100 by ones and by tens.

Name _____

Count by Tens

Essential Question How can you use sets of tens to count to 100?

Lesson 8.8

COMMON CORE STANDARD **CC.K.CC.1**
Know number names and the count sequence.

Listen and Draw REAL WORLD

DIRECTIONS Point to each set of cube towers as you count by tens. Trace the numbers as you count by tens.

Check children's work.

Chapter 8 • Lesson 8

three hundred thirty-seven **337**

Share and Show

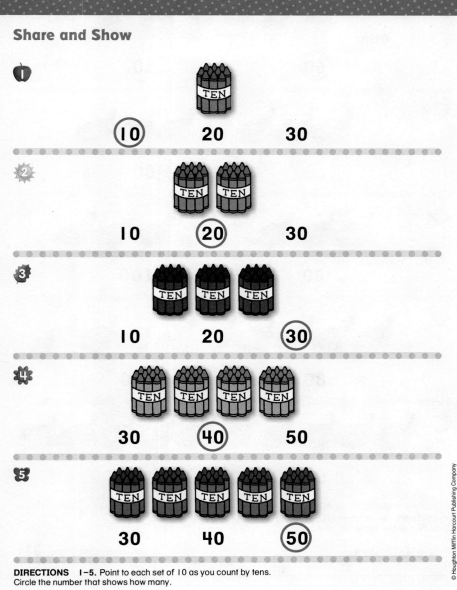

1
(10)   20   30

2
10   (20)   30

3
10   20   (30)

4
30   (40)   50

5
30   40   (50)

DIRECTIONS 1–5. Point to each set of 10 as you count by tens. Circle the number that shows how many.

338 three hundred thirty-eight

► **Share and Show** • **Guided Practice**

Show children 10 crayons. Place a band around the crayons to show a set. Make sure children realize there are 10 crayons in one set.

Discuss the pictures on the page.

• **How are the pictures alike?** They all show 10 crayons in each set.

Have children point to Exercise 1.

• **Point to each set of 10 as you count by tens.** 10

• **How many sets of 10 are there?** 1 **Which number shows how many crayons are in the set?** 10 **Circle the number.**

Have children point to Exercise 2.

• **Point to each set of 10 as you count by tens.** 10, 20

• **How many sets of 10 are there?** 2 **How many do two sets of 10 show?** 20 **Circle the number.**

Have children complete the exercises. Children point to each set of 10 as they count by tens and circle the number that shows how many.

Reteach 8.8

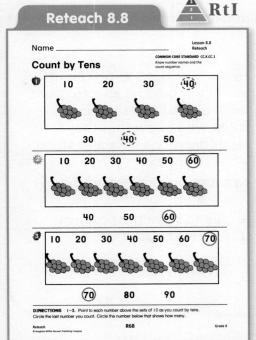

Name _____

Lesson 8.8
Reteach

Count by Tens

COMMON CORE STANDARD CC.K.CC.1
Know number names and the count sequence.

1   10   20   30   (40)
        30   (40)   50

2   10   20   30   40   50   (60)
             40   50   (60)

3   10   20   30   40   50   60   (70)
        (70)   80   90

DIRECTIONS 1–3. Point to each number above the sets of 10 as you count by tens. Circle the last number you count. Circle the number below that shows how many.

Reteach
© Houghton Mifflin Harcourt Publishing Company

R68   Grade K

Enrich 8.8

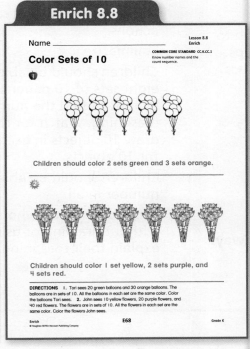

Name _____

Lesson 8.8
Enrich

Color Sets of 10

COMMON CORE STANDARD CC.K.CC.1
Know number names and the count sequence.

1

Children should color 2 sets green and 3 sets orange.

Children should color 1 set yellow, 2 sets purple, and 4 sets red.

DIRECTIONS 1. Tori sees 20 green balloons and 30 orange balloons. The balloons are in sets of 10. All the balloons in each set are the same color. Color the balloons Tori sees. 2. John sees 10 yellow flowers, 20 purple flowers, and 40 red flowers. The flowers are in sets of 10. All the flowers in each set are the same color. Color the flowers John sees.

Enrich
© Houghton Mifflin Harcourt Publishing Company

E68   Grade K

COMMON ERRORS

Error Children may start counting by tens and then count only one more instead of ten more.

Example Children count 10, 11, 12.

Springboard to Learning Show children a hundred chart. Point out that when they count by tens, each ten ends with a zero.

► More Practice

Explain to children that they will count by tens on this page as they did on the last page.

- **What does each set of grapes show?** a set of 10

Have children point to each set of grapes as they count by tens. Have children circle the numbers that shows how many.

Use Exercises 6 and 7 for **Quick Check**.

Quick Check ▲ RtI

If ➤ a child misses Exercises 6 and 7

Then ➤ **Differentiate Instruction** with
- RtI Tier 1 Activity, p. 337B
- Reteach 8.8
- ☆ Soar to Success Math 28.16

H.O.T. Problem A friend gives you 60 crayons but does not say how many. You want to count the crayons. Do you need to count by ones? Explain. Possible answer: No. I can put the crayons in sets of ten and count by tens. 10, 20, 30, 40, 50, 60.

Go Deeper MATHEMATICAL PRACTICES

Children should recognize that they do not need a hundred chart to count by tens. They can place objects in sets of ten and count them by tens.

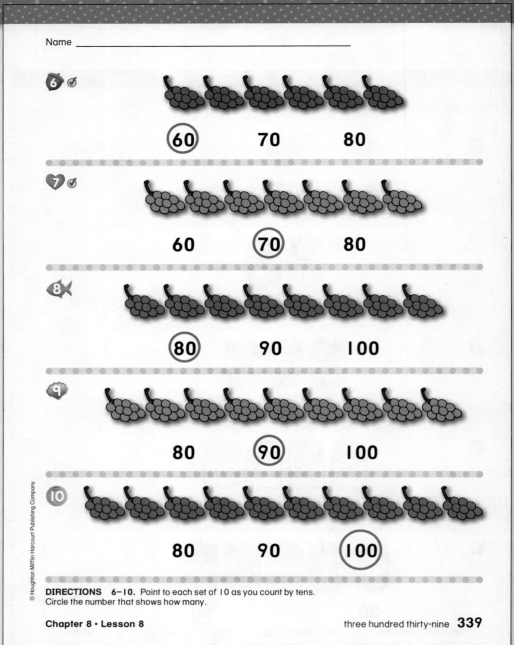

Name _____

6. (60)   70   80

7. 60   (70)   80

8. (80)   90   100

9. 80   (90)   100

10. 80   90   (100)

© Houghton Mifflin Harcourt Publishing Company

DIRECTIONS 6–10. Point to each set of 10 as you count by tens. Circle the number that shows how many.

Chapter 8 • Lesson 8   three hundred thirty-nine **339**

Extend the Math Activity

Count Sets by Tens

Investigate Read this word problem and ask children to solve it by drawing: **Molly has eight sets of paperclips. Each set has 10 paperclips. How many paperclips does Molly have?**

Math Talk

- **What steps will you take to solve this problem?** I can draw a picture to show the eight sets of paper clips. Then I can count the sets by tens.
- **How many paperclips does Molly have?** 80
- **Why do you think your answer makes sense?** Possible answers: I know that when I count by tens 8 times, I get 80.
- **How can you solve this problem in a different way?** Possible answers: I can make cube trains; I can look at a hundred chart; I can draw one object to stand for each set of ten; I can count by tens aloud until I counted 8 times.

As children draw and count, ask them to describe their actions.

Summarize

Children should be able to draw pictures to represent eight sets of 10 paperclips. They should be able to count by tens to find the number in all and explain their reasoning. Watch for children who know that they can draw 10 objects in each set or draw one object to stand for 10 objects.

Children should be able to count by tens to find the number in all.

Look for children who are able to solve the problem without drawing or using models and ask them to explain their reasoning.

PROBLEM SOLVING REAL WORLD

Check children's work.

DIRECTIONS Circle sets of 10 stars. Count the sets of stars by tens.

HOME ACTIVITY • Give your child some macaroni or dried beans and ten cups. Ask him or her to place ten pieces of macaroni into each cup. Then have him or her point to each cup as he or she counts by tens to 100.

© Houghton Mifflin Harcourt Publishing Company

340 three hundred forty

FOR EXTRA PRACTICE: Standards Practice Book, p. P168

FOR MORE PRACTICE: Standards Practice Book, pp. P165–P166

▶ **Problem Solving**

Use questions to guide children through this page. Discuss with children that counting to 100 by tens is faster than counting to 100 by ones.

- **Look at the stars. Circle sets of 10 stars.**

Explain to children that they may circle sets of 10 stars any way they wish. Point out that the placement of stars does not change the number in all. Watch for children who may miscount when they circle sets of 10.

- **How many sets of stars did you circle?** 10 sets
- **Count the sets of stars by tens.** 10, 20, 30, 40, 50, 60, 70, 80, 90, 100 **How many stars are there?** 100
- **How do you know that your answer makes sense?** I counted 10 sets of stars. Ten sets of stars is 100 stars.

④ SUMMARIZE

Essential Question

How can you use sets of tens to count to 100?
I can count each set of ten until I get to 100, 10, 20, 30, 40, 50, 60, 70, 80, 90. 100.

Differentiated Instruction · INDEPENDENT ACTIVITIES

Differentiated Centers Kit

Activities Roundup

Children complete the blue Activity Card 17 by showing sets of 10 objects.

Games
Sweet and Sour Path

Games

Children increase familiarity with numbers from 1 to 30 with repeated counting forward to move along the game path.

Digital Path

- Animated Math Models
- iT iTools
- HMH Mega Math
- Soar to Success Math
- eStudent Edition

Summative Assessment

Use the **Chapter 8 Review/Test** to assess children's progress in Chapter 8.

You may want to review with children the essential question for the chapter.

Chapter Essential Question

How can you show, count, and write numbers to 20 and beyond?

Ask the following questions to focus children's thinking:

- **How can you show and write numbers to 20?**
- **How can you count numbers to 50 by ones? How can you count numbers to 100 by tens?**

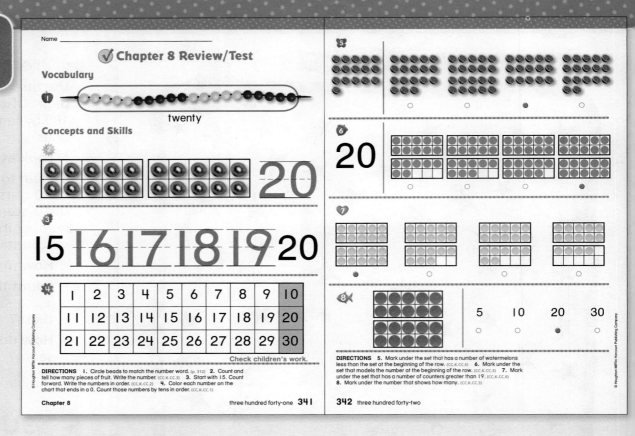

✓ Data-Driven Decision Making ▲ RtI

Based on the results of the Chapter Review/Test, use the following resources to review skills.

Item	Lesson	*CCSS	Common Error	Intervene With	Soar to Success Math
1	8.1	CC.K.CC.5	May have difficulty reading the number	R—8.1; TE—p. 309B	1.09
2	8.2	CC.K.CC.3	May miscount	R—8.2; TE—p. 313B	2.12
3	8.3	CC.K.CC.2	May be confused about ordering numbers	R—8.3; TE—p. 317B	7.13
4	8.7	CC.K.CC.1	May have difficulty reading the hundred chart	R—8.7; TE—p. 333B	28.25
5	8.4	CC.K.CC.6	May have difficulty understanding a number less than	R—8.4; TE—p. 321B	70.01
6	8.2	CC.K.CC.3	May have difficulty identifying the set that shows the number	R—8.2; TE—p. 313B	2.12
7	8.4	CC.K.CC.6	May have difficulty understanding a number greater than	R—8.4; TE—p. 321B	70.01
8	8.2	CC.K.CC.3	May have difficulty identifying how many	R—8.2; TE—p. 313B	2.12
9	8.3	CC.K.CC.2	May have difficulty ordering numbers	R—8.3; TE—p. 317B	7.13
10	8.5	CC.K.CC.1	May have difficulty counting to 50	R—8.5; TE—p. 325B	
11	8.4	CC.K.CC.6	May have difficulty understanding a number greater than	R—8.4; TE—p. 321B	70.01
12	8.8	CC.K.CC.1	May have difficulty identifying the set that shows the number	R—8.8; TE—p. 337B	28.16

*CCSS—Common Core State Standards   **Key: R**—Reteach Book; **TE**—RtI Activities

Name _____

9 11 12 10   13 17 15   14 15 16   15 14 19
   ○   ○   ●   ○

10

1	2	3	4	5	6	7	8	9	10
11	12	13	14	15	16	17	18	19	20
21	22	23	24	25	26	27	28	29	30
31	32	33	34	35	36	37	38	39	40
41	42	43	44	45	46	47	48	49	

40   50   60   70
○   ●   ○   ○

11

   ●   ○   ○   ○

12
TEN TEN TEN TEN TEN TEN TEN TEN

50   60   70   80
○   ○   ○   ●

DIRECTIONS 9. Mark under the numbers that show them in order.
(CC.K.CC.2) **10.** Point to each number as you count. Mark under the number
that completes the counting order. (CC.K.CC.1) **11.** Mark under the set that
has a number of apples greater than the set at the beginning of the row.
(CC.K.CC.6) **12.** Count the crayons by tens. Mark under the number that
shows how many. (CC.K.CC.1)

Chapter 8   three hundred forty-three **343**

Performance Task

_____

_____

_____

Check children's work.

PERFORMANCE TASK This task will assess the child's understanding
of identifying and ordering numbers to 20. (CC.K.CC.1, CC.K.CC.2, CC.K.CC.3,
CC.K.CC.5, CC.K.CC.6)

344 three hundred forty-four

Performance Indicators

A child with a Level 2 paper:

____ counts to 50 by ones.

____ writes three numbers in order from least to greatest.

____ builds a cube train to match the greatest number.

____ identifies the greatest number.

Performance Task Scoring Rubric

2	**Generally accurate, complete, and clear:** All of the parts of the task are successfully completed. There is evidence of clear understanding of the key concepts and procedures. Child's work shows that all answers are correct or reasonable.
1	**Partially accurate:** Some parts of the task are successfully completed; other parts are attempted and their intent addressed, but they are not completed.
0	**Not accurate, complete, and clear:** No part of the task is completed with any success. There is little, if any, evidence that the child understands key concepts and procedures.

Performance Task may be used for portfolios.

Performance Task

Extended Response

Objective Assess the understanding of numbers 20 and beyond.

Materials connecting cubes, Fifty Chart (see *eTeacher Resources*)

Listen and Do

Give each child a fifty chart. Have children count from 1 to 50 in order by ones. Then have them choose one number within 20 and circle it.

• **Which number is one less?**

• **Which number is two greater?**

Write the three numerals in order from least to greatest on your page.

• **Build a cube train to show the greatest number. Draw the cube train.**

• **Circle the number that matches the cube train.**

Use performance indicators, scoring rubric, and DOK level to evaluate conceptual understanding.

Depth of Knowledge

Performance Task	DOK Level
	2

Performance Assessment

Chapters 1-8

See *Assessment Guide* for Performance Tasks to be completed at the end of each critical area.

Chapter 8
Test

Summative Assessment

Use the **Chapter Test** to assess children's progress in Chapter 8.

Chapter Tests are provided in multiple-choice and mixed-response format in the *Assessment Guide*.

GO Online Chapter 8 Test is available online.

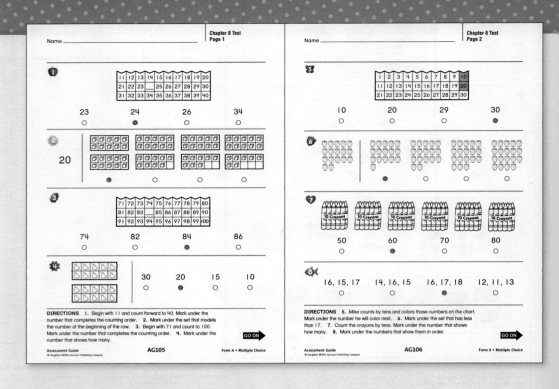

Data-Driven Decision Making RtI

Item	Lesson	*CCSS	Common Error	Intervene With	Soar to Success Math
1, 9	8.5	CC.K.CC.1	May not be able to understand the count sequence	R—8.5; TE—p. 325B	
2, 10	8.1	CC.K.CC.5	May not be able to model 20	R—8.1; TE—p. 309B	1.09
3, 11	8.6	CC.K.CC.1	May not be able to count to 100 using a hundred chart	R—8.6; TE—p. 329B	28.11
4, 12	8.2	CC.K.CC.3	May not understand how to write 20 and count to 20	R—8.2; TE—p. 313B	2.12

***CCSS**—Common Core State Standards   **Key: R**—Reteach Book; **TE**—RtI Activities

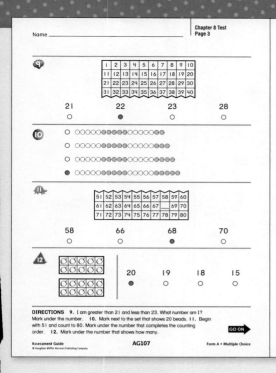

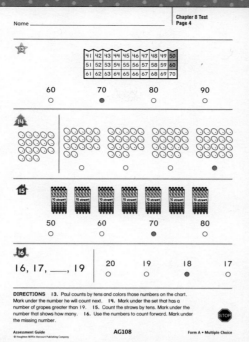

✓ Data-Driven Decision Making RtI

Item	Lesson	*CCSS	Common Error	Intervene With	Soar to Success Math
5, 13	8.7	CC.K.CC.1	May miscount by tens using a hundred chart	R—8.5; TE—p. 333B	28.25
6, 14	8.4	CC.K.CC.6	May not understand terms *more* or *less*	R—8.4; TE—p. 321B	70.01
7, 15	8.8	CC.K.CC.1	May miscount by tens using sets of 10	R—8.8; TE—p. 337B	28.16
8, 16	8.3	CC.K.CC.2	May miscount when counting on from a given number	R—8.3; TE—p. 317B	7.13

*CCSS—Common Core State Standards   **Key: R**—Reteach Book; **TE**—RtI Activities